S0-AFK-298

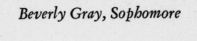

Beverly Gray, Sophomore

The two girls ran all the way from Chadwick Hall!

(BEVERLY GRAY, SOPHOMORE)

BEVERLY GRAY
SOPHOMORE

By CLAIR BLANK

A. L. BURT COMPANY

Publishers

NEW YORK   CHICAGO

The Beverly Gray
College Mystery Series

By CLAIR BLANK

BEVERLY GRAY, FRESHMAN

BEVERLY GRAY, SOPHOMORE

BEVERLY GRAY, JUNIOR

BEVERLY GRAY, SENIOR

COPYRIGHT, 1934, BY
A. L. BURT COMPANY

———

Beverly Gray, Sophomore

PRINTED IN THE U. S. A.

CONTENTS

Contents

CHAPTER I

Alpha Deltas

"Greetings, old pals, old kids, old socks, old things!"

The vivacious young lady who entered her friends' room so boisterously was Lenora Whitehill, commonly known as the campus cut-up. No one could think of more mischief than that which came out of Lenora's bobbed head.

"Greetings, yourself!" answered one of the girls, Shirley Parker, who lounged lazily against the window sill. The setting sun sent little shafts of sunlight dancing in the room and brought forth the reddish tints in her hair.

At the imminent risk of falling on her nose, a slim, laughing young lady was hanging out of the window at a perilous angle, gayly waving to someone on the campus below.

"Beverly Gray! Do you want to fall on your head?" the newcomer demanded.

7

The brown head was withdrawn from the window, and the girl stood up laughing.

"Hello, Lenora," Beverly answered. "Gerry Foster has just arrived."

"Don't you like our new quarters?" Shirley Parker, the red-headed girl, asked, bouncing up and down on her bed. "I think they are just grand!"

"Some class," Lenora murmured in approval, glancing about the room.

The walls were painted a cream color, and pictures and gayly colored school pennants huug thereon. Twin beds were placed close together, one on each side of the window. Two desks, also side by side, stood against the opposite wall. A bright-patterned rug covered the floor, and two chairs were placed at inviting intervals. Cushions were strewn about in profusion.

"Some class," Lenora repeated. "Chadwick Hall the Second certainly does itself proud."

Those who have read *Beverly Gray, Freshman*, are acquainted with Beverly's exciting adventures of her first year at Vernon College, and with her heroic action during the drastic fire that destroyed the first Chadwick Hall. They have also met Beverly's roommate, Shirley Parker. Shirley's first year at Vernon started badly, and she was back now with the firm resolution to get the most out of her sophomore year. The mischievous Lenora Whitehill and her roommate, Rosalie Arnold, are familiar figures, as are Lois Mason and Anne White, Beverly's friend from home.

The door opened and in burst Rosalie, followed hilariously by Anne and Lois.

"What-ho, comrades of Vernon!" Rosalie called gayly. "What do you think of our new mansion?"

"We think it's the berries," Lenora answered promptly if slangily.

"I'm awf'ly glad to be back," Anne sighed, seating herself beside Beverly on the window sill.

"What?" Lenora shouted. "Glad to be back at school? Inhuman girl!"

"I am glad to be back," Anne said again defiantly. "I'll bet you are, too."

"Well——" Lenora conceded.

"Of course, we have to study hard," Lois said, "but we have a lot of fun."

"Will you ever forget the freshman play last year?" Shirley laughed.

"When Lois had to play Romeo, even though she had a black eye," Lenora giggled.

"And the trick we played on the sophomores and juniors at their dance," Anne reminded them.

"We ought to incorporate," Lois declared.

"There is an idea!" Shirley took up the suggestion. "Why don't we form a sorority—or something?"

"Fine!" Beverly applauded. "Let's."

"I nominate Beverly Gray for president," Lenora sang out.

"I second the motion," Anne said promptly. "All those in favor say 'aye'!"

A loud chorus of "ayes" greeted her.

"Beverly Gray, president of the Whatsis Sorority," Lenora said, leading Beverly to her desk and installing her therein.

"The meeting will please come to order!" the new president said, rapping on the desk. "I think the first thing to be decided is the name for our new organization. Has anyone any suggestions?"

"Sunshine Club."

"Mischief Makers."

"Vernon Girls."

"Rainbow Girls."

The suggestions poured forth from all present until the president rapped for silence again.

"All the names are good," Beverly said, "but —let's have something more dignified."

"As befitting sophomores," Lenora interrupted.

"I know we are all full of mischief," Beverly said, smiling, "and I know we are always cheerful——"

"Oh, yeah?" criticized the irrepressible Lenora.

"But I also think," Beverly continued, ignoring the interruption, "that once in a while we should be serious. We want our sorority to last years from now, so we should have a more suitable name for a sorority."

"A Greek name," Lois contributed.

"Yes," Beverly acknowledged, "a Greek name would be nice."

"How about Alpha Epsilon?"

"Or Delta Omega?"

"Alpha Delta," Anne contributed.

"We'll vote on it," Rosalie suggested.

Shirley distributed paper and pencils, and each girl wrote down her choice of name. Then the slips were collected, and Lenora and Anne sorted out the votes to determine the winner.

"From now on," Lenora said impressively, "this group of young ladies will be known as the Alpha Delta Sorority."

"Now about the other officers of this august body," Beverly began.

"Madam Chairman, may I have the floor?" Shirley asked.

Beverly nodded, and Shirley stood up.

"I don't think we need any other officers right now," she said.

"Nor I," Lenora murmured out of turn. "Wait until we start having business."

"We need a secretary," Anne pointed out.

"I think Shirley was talking," Beverly reminded the others.

"I was going to suggest that we have but two meetings a term," Shirley said. "One meeting on the first day we are back, and one on the last day before vacation. If, for some reason, any of us want a meeting, we can call a special one."

"That is where the secretary comes in," Anne said again.

"All in favor of the course Shirley suggested say 'aye,' " Beverly directed.

A chorus of "ayes" greeted her.

"And now to elect a secretary," Beverly said. "Shall we vote on it?"

Once more the slips of paper were distributed and collected.

"Lois is now the secretary of the Alpha Delta Sorority," Lenora announced.

"Madam President, I have a suggestion to make," Lenora said, and by the humorous glint in her eyes Beverly knew it would be a mischievous one. "I think," Lenora continued, "that we should try to find something interesting to do this term."

"Such as——"

"Anything that would be fun," Lenora answered. "I have no particular suggestion in mind."

"'Therefore," Beverly said, "the aim of this sorority is——"

"Anything that is fun," Lois supplied, "or entertaining."

"Where are we going to find it?" Anne wanted to know.

"There is the Sophomore Dance on Hallowe'en," Rosalie said. "Perhaps we could think up something spectacular for that."

"We'll try," Shirley promised.

The loud peals of a bell rang through the building, and the meeting was abruptly brought to a close as the girls hurried to the dining room for their dinner. After dinner the girls gathered in the main living room of Chadwick Hall and sang songs to the accompaniment of the piano.

Studies would not begin until the morrow, and the girls crowded all the chatter and laughter they could into their first night together. The term promised difficult school work, but it also promised fun and mystery, the latter in which Beverly and her friends were to figure largely.

CHAPTER II

An Assignment

"I MADE it!" Beverly announced, bursting in upon Anne, Lenora, and Shirley, who were laboring over a difficult literature lesson.

"You made what?" Lenora demanded.

"I made the staff of the *Comet!*" Beverly repeated ecstatically. The *Comet* was the college newspaper, and Beverly had desired nothing so much as to be on the staff. "You are now gazing on a reporter of our estimable college newspaper."

"Congratulations!" Shirley said smilingly. "What is your first assignment?"

"You know the old Horler Mansion at the end of College Avenue?" Beverly asked.

"Yes," the three acknowledged.

"Well, lately several people in Vernon have said they saw strange lights and figures moving about in the old house. I'm to go and see if there are any —ghosts."

"Ooooo!" Anne shivered. "I wouldn't like that."

"If you see any, give them my regards," Lenora said gayly.

"Be sure and be back in time for dinner," Shirley called as with a flourish of her notebook and pencil Beverly departed on her assignment.

During her first term at Vernon Beverly discovered that she had a desire and a talent to write. Since then she had been bending every effort to secure a position on the college paper. Her position as a reporter on the *Comet* was the first step in the literary career she planned for herself. After college she had dreams of being a reporter on a large newspaper; perhaps eventually she might be a foreign correspondent, reporting stories from Europe, Asia, the South Seas—who knew?

College had been in session now a week, and this was the first thing that had happened to break the regular routine of studies. Beverly stepped along the Avenue briskly. She was glad to have something to divert her thoughts from classrooms for a little while. The assignment too, savored of mystery. That intrigued her as nothing else would have done. Alison Cox, editor of the *Comet*, had not wanted to give her this job of reporting on the supposedly haunted house, but Beverly had coaxed and wheedled until in sheer self-defense Alison had given in.

The Horler Mansion sat far back from the road. It was surrounded by a dense growth of underbrush and trees. The house was gray and weather stained from the winds and rains that beat upon it. More than one shutter was hanging by a single rusty hinge. The roof was peaked and gabled, and two broken brick chimneys towered like stumps against the blue sky. The porch was rotting into decay, and the windows were like bleak eyes staring into nothingness.

Andrew Horler had built the mansion for his bride in 1870. When his son was married, he too brought his bride there to live. In those days it was painted a dazzling white, and laughter and gay voices echoed within its walls. When the son died, he had no heir to succeed him, so the place was put up for auction.

The mansion passed into the hands of an old man and was painted a depressing gray. The new owner was a figure of mystery to all the surrounding country. People were very seldom allowed to catch a glimpse of him, for he lived the secluded life of a hermit. Wild tales spread about the country that the old man was rich and was living this secluded life because he had a large treasure concealed somewhere in the house. He was supposed to have a large chest of gold and precious loot that had been taken off a pirate ship. Nothing was heard to sub-

stantiate these tales, but they persisted, neverthe-
less. Then, one dark and stormy night, a marauder
broke in. Through the shadows he glided up to the
old man's bedroom, where, the tales had it, the old
man kept his chest of gold.

In the morning an inquisitive neighbor found
the front door swinging open and a strange still-
ness upon the place. Curiously, the man entered
and went through the empty rooms until he came
to a bedroom, where he found the body of the old
man. He was dead, with a knife sticking right
through his heart. The neighbor fled in terror to
the authorities. The police came and viewed the
situation, but no clues were found as to the iden-
tity of the murderer, nor had the house been ran-
sacked to prove that the marauder had searched for
the treasure.

From that time to this, legend had it that the
place was haunted. The old man was supposed to
come back to guard his treasure, although no one
had actually seen him. For years nothing had been
heard from the old house until recently. Now people began whispering about lights and figures seen
at night moving about in the rooms. One man had
seen strange men carrying in boxes, yet when he
and a policeman went to investigate, no boxes
could be found. Too, voices, high and singsongy,
were heard coming from the shadows. It was a

mystery that had the town of Vernon all a-twitter.

Beverly approached the mansion from the road. She cut through brambles and bushes that threatened dire damage to her silk stockings, and stood for a moment before the house. It was silent and deserted. A slight wind stirred amid the tall grass and set the leaves on the trees to whispering. She jotted down a few notes in her little notebook and climbed the broken steps to the rotting porch. She tiptoed to the windows. It wasn't necessary to tiptoe, but she felt a strong aversion to making any noise. She smilingly told herself that a loud noise might awaken the ghosts.

She cleared a place on the rain-spattered glass of the window and looked in. A room, large, empty, and exceedingly dusty, met her gaze. In one corner stood a huge fireplace and before it a rickety wooden box. That was all. At one end were huge wooden doors, closed.

Well, she could get no material for a story from that room. She would have to go in and investigate farther. She approached the door and turned the knob. It swung open at her lightest touch. Damp, musty air rushed out and met her. Tremulously she set foot in the dark hall. In order to have some light while she conducted her tour of the building, she left the door standing ajar. Cautiously she advanced step by step.

To her right were the huge doors leading into the front room that she had seen when she looked in the window. No need to go in there, for she already knew everything that was to be found. To her left was another set of high wooden doors. She approached them and pushed on one. It swung inward on squeaky hinges. She put her head into the opening and looked around.

The room was heavily shuttered, but light seeped in from one window, where the shutter was dislodged. This room, too, was empty of furniture, but large shelves lined the walls. Evidently it had once been used as a library. Dust, thick and undisturbed, lay over everything.

Beverly retreated and closed the door again. Once more she stood in the hall. It was uncannily black in here. She looked toward the front door. It was shut! Had the wind blown it shut or had some more human agency been at work?

CHAPTER III

Head Ghost

SHE remembered, then, that the wind had scarcely been strong enough this afternoon to blow such a heavy door shut—without a sound. If it had banged shut, she would have heard it. She felt out with her hand and touched the wall. With her back to it she stood still, straining her ears for a sound that would tell her she was not alone in this black hallway.

A sudden scurrying movement sent her heart leaping into her throat. Something small and fuzzy touched her foot. A mouse! She laughed with relief as her nerves relaxed. Naturally an old deserted house such as this would have mice. That was nothing to frighten her. Why did she insist on imagining things? Still, a mouse could not have shut the door. Why did that thought persist in troubling her?

She turned and made her way, slowly and as silently as she could, into the dining room. The furnishings still stood in this room as they must have stood when the queer old man had lived in the house. The three-piece dining-room suite, heavy oak and old-fashioned, was showing the ravages of age. Even the cloth on the table was rotting slowly into threads. There were plates on the table, some covered with dust and some that were not. The latter interested Beverly. Evidently three people had dined, in style, at the old-fashioned table—and lately! Glasses still partly filled with water, a half loaf of bread, not at all old and mouldy, and an ash tray filled with partly smoked cigarettes gave evidence of what must have been not a very pretentious meal.

Into the little notebook went more notes as Beverly took in every detail of the room. Who could have been living in the house? Was it the explanation to all those queer lights and figures that had been seen? Anyway the "ghosts" were humans, needing a substantial meal just as any other person. A trace of cigarette smoke still lingered in the air. Beverly sniffed it in a puzzled manner. How long had the "ghosts" been gone, if they were gone? Not very long, of that she was sure. She turned from her survey of the dining table and stopped terrified in her tracks.

There, standing in the doorway through which

she had entered, was a man. A man not at all prepossessing in appearance. He wore no hat, and his hair was straggling and unkempt. His shirt was dirty and his trousers creaseless. From his crooked mouth dangled a cigarette. A long, evil-looking scar ran from the point of his chin to the tip of his left ear.

"Well," he drawled, "whada you want?"

"I—um—that is—I'm from the college, and I was sent out to get a story on this old house for our newspaper," Beverly said with a winning smile.

"Yeah?" he sneered, ignoring her friendliness. "Well, you can get out. This old house isn't nice to visitors."

"I shan't go until I get my story," Beverly said confidently. "I would only have to come back again."

"You better get out," he said menacingly. "Aren't you afraid of the ghosts?"

"Ghosts?" Beverly said innocently, as if she had never heard the word before. "Are you one of them?"

He laughed as if at a great joke. "Yeah. Yeah, sure. I'm the head ghost."

"How many more are there?" Beverly asked.

"I don't know right offhand," he said with a cruel smile. "Come on, you're getting out now."

The man grasped her arm and propelled her

roughly to the front door. He swung it open and pushed her out onto the porch.

"And don't come back!" he said glaring at her.

With great nonchalance Beverly straightened the beret that he had pushed awry and smiled. "You're not very cordial to your guests, are you?"

"Not to the guests who don't knock," he retorted. "Get going!"

For a minute Beverly stood undecided. She had to get a story. If she went back and told Alison and the rest she had been put off the premises the girls wouldn't believe her. No one was known to be living in the house. She would be the laughing stock of the college. She looked again at the villainous person standing squarely in the doorway. Not much chance of getting past him. Then an idea occurred to her, and she almost smiled gleefully.

"You shouldn't leave the front door unlocked," she shot back at him. "I warn you, I'll be back."

"I'm goin' to stay right here and see that you don't get in again," he said, establishing himself in a comfortable position on the doorstep.

That was just what she had been angling for. If he would stay there at the front of the house, perhaps she could get in through the kitchen. She smiled jauntily and stepped down off the porch. She proceeded on her way toward the road, her notebook tucked cozily under her arm. Several

yards from the house the bushes and trees hid her
from the man's view. It was then she doubled back.
She kept in the shadows of the trees and out of
range of the man's vision.

Creeping along, she came to the back of the
house. She stood for several minutes looking over
the building. She didn't want to walk into any
more ghosts. When she had first seen that man
standing so calmly staring at her there in the dining room her heart had skipped a couple of beats.
She had supposed she was alone in the place, and
then to come face to face with such a rough-look-
ing character—it was hair-raising.

Satisfied that no one was stirring in the rear of
the building she crept up to the kitchen door. It
was locked! Luck was against her. She took stock
of her position. There was a small window, just
large enough for her to squeeze through, high up
near the roof of the kitchen. It no doubt opened
inward over the kitchen sink. Now, if she could
find something to stand on—— She spied a heavy
rain barrel. Just the thing! Some kind and con-
siderate soul had already turned it upside down.
If she could roll it over under the window and
somehow manage to get the window open——
With a mighty effort and considerable damage to
her white sports dress, she managed to shove the
barrel into position. With a leap she was up on top
of it and at work on the window. The lock was

old and rusty, and it didn't take much of an effort on her part to break it.

This was fun, breaking into a haunted house. Most people were content never to go near such a place, but Beverly, now that one ghost, the head ghost, had proved to be so human, could find no fear. The window swung inward, as she had thought it would do. It was a tight squeeze to get her lithe body through the narrow opening, but she managed it. She had been right in her guess. The sink was directly under the window. In another second she stood in the middle of the kitchen gazing in surprise at the stock of provisions that met her gaze. Under the sink and in the old-fashioned kitchen cabinet were cans upon cans of foodstuffs. The ghosts were indeed well supplied. Milk bottles, some empty, some not empty, were lined along the floor; wax papers and newspapers were strewn about, as were dirty dishes. Evidently, dish washing was not one of the ghosts' accomplishments.

Beverly tiptoed to the swinging door that communicated with the dining room. She put her ear to the panel and listened. Not a sound. The head ghost must still be sitting on the front-door step. Inch by inch she opened the door and slipped through. There was nothing left to explore on the first floor, so she started for the stairs that led to the floor overhead. To reach them she must needs

go into the hall, and that might mean discovery
by the head ghost. On tiptoe and holding her
breath lest he suddenly decide to come into the
house, Beverly reached and went up the stairs.
Now and then they squeaked protestingly beneath
her weight, but evidently the head ghost didn't
hear the squeaks and groans, for he did not investigate.

She reached the second floor and viewed the
closed doors that confronted her. Four doors behind which lay—what? Which one should she
choose first? She might as well start at one end of
the hall and continue on until she had entered each
room. She chose the door at the front end of the
hall. It opened into a large, empty room that at one
time had been the master bedroom. There was
nothing there to excite her interest, so she continued on to the second.

In the second room she found a bed, dirty and
disreputable. It had recently been slept in, too, for
a blanket and an old tattered comforter were piled
unceremoniously in a heap. Was this the boudoir of
the head ghost? It would seem so. Aside from more
newspapers scattered over the floor, there was
nothing to interest her, so she left that room.

The third room she entered was dark. Heavy
shutters kept out any light. She could make out
nothing in the indistinct darkness, so she did not
linger there. The fourth room was small, little

more than a closet. In one corner were steps leading up to the attic. Without hesitation she crossed
to them and started to mount. A trapdoor opened
in the ceiling, and through this she crawled into
another small room. All the light there was in
here came through a skylight in the ceiling. In one
corner and scattered about were piled boxes.
Beverly investigated one of these. It contained pink
packets filled with a finely ground powder. Some
also contained small round pills. Beverly little real-
ized, then, the significance of her discovery.

Dinner at Chadwick Hall was promptly at six
o'clock, and anyone late was the object of a series
of black looks from Mrs. Dennis and the other
teachers. Beverly looked at her watch and frowned.
It was five-thirty. She had just a half hour in which
to return to Chadwick Hall and make herself pre-
sentable. If she dared to appear at the dinner table
with her dress in the condition it was she would be
disgraced.

Tearing herself away from her discovery and
mentally promising to come back on the morrow,
Beverly descended to the second floor again, clos-
ing the trapdoor after her. Heavy footsteps were
ascending the stairs. In the little closet-like room
Beverly held her breath and listened. The head
ghost must have gotten tired of his sentinel duty
at the front door. He was coming up to the second
floor. Was he coming to the little room in which

she stood? The footsteps paused at the head of the stairs and then went down the hall. No! She breathed easier. He was going to his makeshift bedroom. She would have to wait until he went down the stairs again before she dared to make a noise.

Slow minutes passed while Beverly listened to the sounds the head ghost made. If only he would go downstairs so she could also descend. She would most surely be late for dinner! He was staying an awf'ly long time. She opened the door and peeped cautiously out into the hall. His door stood ajar. If he happened to look out as she was creeping toward the stairs, he would be sure to see her. She had to take that chance. She couldn't stand here all night.

Step by step, moving cautiously so as not to step on a squeaky board, Beverly tiptoed to the stairs. So far so good! But the steps were old, and she remembered how they had squeaked when she mounted them. One, two—oh, she almost stumbled that time! three, four—darn that step! five, six—— There were fifteen steps in all, and Beverly breathed a sigh of relief when she reached the bottom. She would leave by the front door. She tiptoed down the hall and tried it. It was locked! The head ghost was taking no chances on any more surprise visitors. She would have to leave the way she entered—via the sink and the rain barrel.

CHAPTER IV

Found—One Mystery

"WHAT do you mean, Beverly Gray, by this crazy statement?" Alison Cox, the editor of the *Comet*, demanded as she read the story Beverly had submitted about the old haunted house.

"Which one is that?" Beverly asked laughingly as she seated herself on the edge of Alison's desk.

" 'The chief sustenance of the ghosts seems to be baked beans and coffee,' " Alison quoted. "There is no sense to it."

"Well, there were piles of bean and coffee cans in the kitchen," Beverly maintained.

"Probably covered with dust," Alison said.

"They were not!" Beverly said indignantly. "They were all fresh. I tell you, Alison, there is something mysterious about that house. I told you about the man I saw there. Certainly he was no ghost." She giggled. "Although he said he was," she added.

"Only a tramp," Alison said, refusing to be roused to any excitement.

"For a tramp he had a lot of provisions," Beverly commented. "I'm sure there is a good story for the paper to be had there."

"Well, if you can find something to write about in that old dusty place, you may," Alison sighed. "I still think you are wasting your time."

"I don't think so," Beverly maintained. "If he was only a tramp, why did he try to keep me out of the place?"

"Probably because he likes peace and quiet," was Alison's response.

"More likely because he had something to hide," Beverly said shrewdly.

"He didn't want you to see the baked beans," Alison smiled.

"Silly!" Beverly scoffed. "Just the same, I mean to find out what is going on in that house. I have a feeling that it is something exciting."

"Don't let the ghosts catch you," Alison laughed.

"Wait and see if I don't write a 'scoop' for the newspaper on the doings in that house," Beverly replied confidently.

"Go ahead," Alison said. "I give you a free hand to report on anything interesting that you may see in the mansion."

"O. K.," Beverly said, jumping to her feet, "and I'm going to get some assistants."

That afternoon, the day after she had visited the old house, she called a special meeting of the Alpha Delta Sorority. The girls assembled in Beverly's and Shirley's room immediately after classes, all agog with excitement.

"What's up?" Lenora demanded.

"Yes, why the special session?" Lois wanted to know.

"At the last meeting I believe we made our aim to discover something interesting to do this term," Beverly began.

"Yes, and we have all failed," Lenora said. "There is not a thing that would excite a mouse!"

"I don't know about that," Beverly said smiling. "I had quite an interesting time yesterday."

"You mean you have found something for us to do?" Lenora pounced on her eagerly. "Beverly Gray, if you have found something to break up the monotony, I shall be your friend for life."

"I've found a friend," Beverly said with satisfaction. "You all know the Horler Mansion?"

"Where you had to go for your first assignment on the *Comet*," Shirley contributed.

"The place is dead," Lenora said in disappointment. "I hope you don't expect us to get excited over that musty place. There hasn't been anything doing there since Vernon College started in the nineteenth century."

"That's what you think," Beverly answered, whereat all the girls looked up with interest.

"What do you mean?" Anne asked.

"Yes, tell us about it," Rosalie seconded.

Beverly told them about her explorations. With lurid details she described the man she had met and her forced entrance to the house through the kitchen window. The girls held their breath when she described how she had waited in the little dusty room for the man to discover her hiding place.

"What would have happened if he had discovered you, Beverly?" Lois wondered aloud.

"He would probably have thrown me out on my ear," Beverly said promptly.

"Maybe he would have kept you there," Rosalie said, wide-eyed.

"Be your age," Lenora said slangily. "Why should he keep her there? She didn't do anything."

"But she could tell the authorities about his being there," Anne reminded the other girl.

"She could do that anyway," Lois cut in. "It must have been exciting."

"It was," Beverly assured them. "When I came back and told Alison Cox, she refused to believe there was anything mysterious about the place. She has assigned me to dig up something interesting, if I can."

"Goody, can we help?" Lenora asked excitedly. "A nice juicy mystery is just what I've been looking for."

"That's why I called this special meeting," Beverly said. "I thought we could take turns watching and exploring the place until we find out what the strange lights and figures are that the village people have been talking about."

"We had better plan a campaign," Lois said. "Most of the strange lights are seen at night, aren't they?"

"Yes."

"Tonight Lois and I will go out," Lenora said. "We'll see what we can see. Tomorrow night——"

"Beverly and I will go," Shirley spoke up.

"And the next night, Anne and I," Rosalie suggested. "In that way we ought to discover something."

"I can hardly wait." Lenora danced about the room. "I was so afraid nothing would turn up to save us all from boredom, and here is a nice mystery thrown at us."

"We might get more than we bargain for," Beverly said hesitantly.

"We can handle anything," Lenora said modestly.

"Sure," Lois seconded. "Why be afraid of a few ghosts?"

"I don't mind human ghosts," Rosalie began.

Lenora fixed her roommate with a stern eye. "Who ever heard of a human ghost? They are all supernatural."

"Beverly's head ghost wasn't," Rosalie reminded her.

"He wasn't a ghost, either," Lenora shot back.

"Well, girls," Beverly stood up. "Tonight you had better take flashlights and—go prepare to meet your fate," she added mischievously.

"Oooooo, doesn't she sound cheerful?" Rosalie wailed.

CHAPTER V

Dancing Skeletons

"LENORA WHITEHILL, will you stop sloshing about in those galoshes?" Beverly demanded. "Look at the rug!"

"Well, I can't walk on the ceiling," Lenora shot back.

"You can take them off," Beverly said. "Now," as Lenora took off the offending galoshes and resumed her pacing, "what is all this about?"

"Lois and I went to the Horler Mansion last night," Lenora began.

"Shirley and I go tonight," Beverly added.

"And—" Lenora stopped in the middle of the room and stared at Beverly—"we saw a skeleton dance!"

"You saw a what?" Beverly demanded in amazement.

"We saw a skeleton dance," Lenora repeated, her face troubled. "I don't mind admitting that I was scared out of ten years' growth."

"Be sensible," Beverly said, leaning back in her chair and smiling at her troubled friend. "Skeletons don't dance."

"These did," Lenora maintained. "There were about ten of them, and they performed the most astonishing antics that I ever saw."

"Did Lois see them too?" Beverly asked.

"Yes," Lenora smiled, "so I wasn't the only victim of the hallucination."

"Start at the beginning of the story and tell me about it," Beverly advised.

"Well, Lois and I waited until the lights-out bell had rung at ten o'clock, and then we stole out of the Hall. We walked out College Avenue to where you cut across the field that leads to the Horler Mansion. The moon was hidden behind the clouds, and it was so dark that we couldn't see our hands before our faces. You can be sure we kept close together," Lenora added with a smile. "When we came within sight of the house we saw lights moving about in the front room on the first floor. There was no noise, nor was there anyone to be seen. We crept up to the porch. No one saw us—at least, no one said anything to us, so we went and looked in the windows." Lenora paused and stared out the window, where the rain was teeming down on the green campus.

"Go on," Beverly said breathlessly.

"I'll never forget that sight as long as I live," Lenore said eloquently. "I know Lois won't, either. In the middle of the room were two lanterns, and about them were gathered ten skeletons. As we watched they began to dance, if you could call it a dance," she added half laughingly. "They swayed and jumped and skipped, and all the time their bones were shining in the light from the lanterns."

"It sounds incredible!" Beverly gasped.

"That is what we saw," Lenora said, sitting down and staring at Beverly helplessly. "Needless to say, we got away from there as fast as we could. We came back to the Hall, and I even dreamt about skeletons," she finished.

"Did you tell the other girls about it?" Beverly asked.

"Of course I did," Lenora chattered. "I was so scared I couldn't keep it to myself."

"Do you think we had better give up trying to solve the mystery of the mansion?" Beverly asked.

"No!" Lenora exploded. "I might have been scared last night, but in a day or so I'll be quite ready to go out there again."

"Fine!" Beverly applauded. "You have me all a-quiver. I can hardly wait to see what will face Shirley and me tonight."

"I wouldn't stay very long, whatever it is," Lenora said eloquently.

"Did you see the man I told you about?" Beverly asked.

"After we saw the skeletons we didn't look for anything else," Lenora said promptly. "We came away from that house as fast as our legs would carry us!"

"I don't blame you," Beverly said. "I hope it stops raining before tonight," she added.

The rain stopped before Shirley and Beverly were ready to leave on their adventure, but the sky was clouded over, and the moon was not to be seen. When the lights-out bell rang, Beverly and Shirley, each armed with a flashlight, crept down the stairs and out of the Hall. They walked rapidly along College Avenue until they came to the place where they must cut across the field to come to the mansion.

"I'm getting sh-shivery," Shirley whispered. "D-do you suppose we'll see the skeletons?"

Beverly laughed nervously. "I don't know," she whispered back. "We'll have to wait and see."

They entered the growth of bushes and trees and crept noiselessly toward the house. It was pitch dark here in the fields, and they stumbled more than once over tangled roots and vines. The leaves whispered eerily in the night, and once an owl hooted close to them, scaring them so that they

almost turned and ran back the way they had
come.

The house loomed up before them like a black
cloud in the night. They paused, ready for flight,
and surveyed it. A flicker of light danced momen-
tarily before the front windows.

"The g-ghosts are there," Shirley whispered
tensely.

"It l-looks like it," Beverly agreed through chat-
tering teeth.

"Sh-shall we go up and look in the window?"
Shirley asked again.

Beverly nodded, and together, like two shadows,
the girls stole up the broken steps onto the porch
and stood before the windows.

Their startled vision beheld a room filled with
the most ghastly figures they had ever seen or ever
hoped to see. In the center of the room, about three
feet apart, stood two lanterns lighted and smoking
badly. About them were gathered skeletons, ten of
them. Some were tall, and some not so tall, but
each one's bones gleamed in the flickering light. As
the girls watched, the skulls seemed to grin more
broadly, and the bones began to sway from side to
side. The skeletons seemed to grow in stature and
then to shrink into themselves. From somewhere
in the room came a low moan that gradually grew
into a piercing shriek. The skeletons began to move

about the room, taking queer jerky steps and at the same time making chill-provoking groans and murmurs.

"L-let's get out of here," Shirley whispered in terror, gripping Beverly's arm in fright.

However, they stayed for several more minutes watching the dreadful spectacle. They stayed until a skeleton raised a bony arm and pointed to the window where they were. As the skull seemed to leer at them and come ever closer the two girls turned and fled. They ran as fast as they could through the trees, across the field to the road, where they were forced to halt to get their breath. They regarded one another with wide, terror-stricken glances.

"N-now I believe Lenora," Beverly said between gasps.

"Did you ever see anything so horrible in your whole life?" Shirley murmured awe-stricken.

Beverly shook her head. She never had. The sight of those white, gleaming bones doing their fantastic dance had literally stood her hair on end.

"Do you think they might have followed us?" Shirley demanded, glancing apprehensively over her shoulder.

"It's not likely," Beverly answered. She was frowning at herself. She and Shirley had behaved just like two silly children. They had run away in

panic, when, if they had stayed, they might have
solved the mystery of the house. A memory of the
skeleton that had been coming toward them came
to her, and she knew she couldn't have stayed—
not even to solve a hundred mysteries. Almost
against her will she turned to Shirley.

"Let's go back," she suggested.

"G-go back?" Shirley repeated as if she had not
heard aright.

"Yes, to see if they are still there."

"Oh, no! You won't get me within a hundred
yards of that place again tonight!" Shirley declared
fervently. "I've had enough excitement for one
night. Wait until it is daylight and I'll go back
with you."

"Oh, come on," Beverly urged. "We won't go
up to the house, just to the edge of the trees from
where we can see the lights."

"No!" Shirley declared positively.

"Then I'm going alone," Beverly declared.

"Oh, Beverly, I wish you wouldn't," Shirley
wailed. "I don't want to see you go alone and yet
I'm—scared to go with you."

"Either wait here for me or come along,"
Beverly insisted.

"I'll come," Shirley said at last reluctantly. "But,
remember, not up to the house."

The two crept back the way they had come. The

moon had come out from behind a cloud, and its rays, though not very strong, threw some light along their way. They were afraid to use their flashlights for fear they would be seen from the house, so stumbled along in the light from the moon. They came to the edge of the trees and halted. They gripped each other's arms in tense silence. Walking from the house were two skeletons. The moon shone on them for a moment, and then hid behind the cloud, but even in the darkness their bones gleamed white.

A heavy laugh that sounded strangely familiar to Beverly smote the air, and the skeletons turned to face one another. Voices came from somewhere in their vicinity, and the girls exchanged startled glances. Were these the voices of the skeletons?

"We sure scared those kids," the first voice declared between uproarious booms of laughter.

"I'll bet they're running yet," the second agreed.

More startled glances were exchanged between Beverly and Shirley. Were the skeletons actually discussing them? What was the explanation of these strange voices that seemed to come out of the very air? The skeletons turned and went into the house again.

"L-let's go back to the Hall," Shirley whispered frantically.

All the way back to Chadwick Hall Beverly's

mind was busily trying to find some logical explanation of the skeleton dance. Sound reasoning told
her there were no skeletons that could dance and
talk just like humans. What then was the interpretation of what they had seen?

CHAPTER VI

Larry

THE next afternoon found Beverly again walking along College Avenue out to the old Horler Mansion. She and Lenora and Shirley and Lois had talked over the skeleton dance in a vain attempt to find answers to their mystified questions, but no explanation would come. This afternoon, if she could gain entrance to the house, she would investigate that front room where they had seen the ghosts and see if she could learn something from it.

She went through the trees and across the field to the house. It looked perfectly harmless in the light of day. It looked, too, she thought, much larger from the outside than it was when she was in it. Not a soul was stirring that she could see. She decided not to try the front door today, the head ghost might still be lurking near it to see that she did not enter again. Instead she would resort to the rain barrel and the window.

Beverly walked around to the back of the house. The barrel was just where she had left it. She climbed up on it and opened the window. In another minute she was inside the house. The kitchen was more dirty than she had remembered it from her last visit. She crossed to the swinging door and peeped into the dining room. Like the kitchen, it was deserted. She was through it in a minute and stepping into the dark hall. Boldly she flashed her electric lamp about her. The hall, too, was deserted, and there was no sound of anyone stirring on the floor overhead. She seemed to be alone in the house.

She walked to the large wooden door that led into the front room where the skeleton dance had been held. It took a mighty push to swing the door inward far enough for her to squeeze into the room. She held her breath, half expecting to see the skeletons rise up from the floor and jeer at her. But the room was empty save for the two lanterns that had been lit last night and now stood in a deserted corner. Beverly walked around examining the walls and floor boards for a trapdoor or a sliding panel. She had read stories about old houses that had mysterious hidden rooms and staircases. Perhaps this house had a hidden room into which the skeletons retreated in the daytime to dance forth and make merry at night. But she could find nothing to substantiate this theory. The walls, when she rapped experimentally on them, seemed to be sound enough. She tested the bricks on the fireplace by pushing and tapping them, but nothing happened. No hidden panel slid back to expose a yawning cavity that she might explore.

She stood undecided in the middle of the floor. There certainly was nothing here. She decided to have another look at the mysterious boxes she had discovered in that little attic room the other day. She left the front room and closed the door behind her. Silently, except for the squeaks from the steps, she made her way to the second floor and thence through the trapdoor to the attic room. Lo and behold, all the boxes were gone! Where the piled boxes of mysterious packages of powder had been was now only empty space. This was rather like a game of hide and seek. One time you saw them and the next time you didn't. Who could have removed them? The head ghost? It seemed most likely that the head ghost had taken the boxes with him when he left the house. Where had he gone and would he return? There was nothing to keep her in the little room any longer, so Beverly turned and made her way down to the first floor again. Her search today had yielded nothing. She might as well go back to Chadwick Hall. She would wait a few days and then come back; something might happen in the meantime. To night was Anne's and Rosalie's

KU-301-330

TULA PINK'S CITY SAMPLER

100 MODERN QUILT BLOCKS

D&C

David and Charles

CINCINNATI, OHIO

Table of Contents

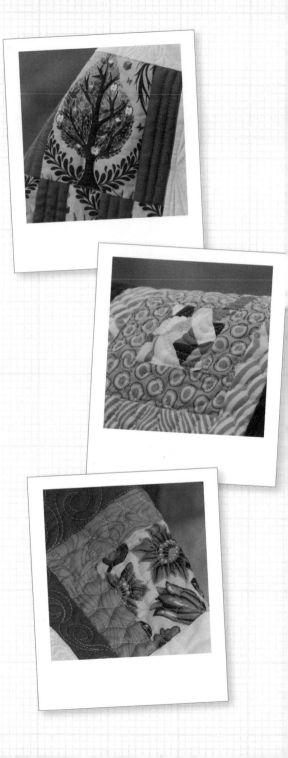

Introduction

We are in a new era of quilting. There has been an infusion of first generation sewers that is unlike anything anyone anticipated.

This may mean that many of you, like me, do not come from a long line of quilters. The art of quilting may not have been passed down through the generations. You may not have a closet full of vintage quilts made by family members who have long since passed away.

I know I don't have these things. I envy those who have a closet full of stories, a treasure trove of family history to warm them in the winter or to use as picnic blankets in the summer. I can cry about it and curse my grandmother for loving shopping more than making, or I can begin to make my own history. I can tell the story of my world the way it is now and pass that down my own little branch of the family tree.

Traditionally, sampler quilts are narratives. They tell the story of a movement or a relationship or a period of time. They tell the stories of battles fought and freedom won. In essence, they are a collection of like things. When we re-create one of these sampler quilts, we are telling someone else's story or, more often, simply re-creating a theme in the style of the past.

I love these antique quilts. They are beautiful and intricate, and they are what initially drew me to quilting. The problem that I have when I sit down to make one of these quilts is that they don't tell my story. I have a visual connection to them but not an emotional one. This book intends to rectify that for those who feel the same as I do.

You will notice in the following pages that the blocks are not named but simply numbered. This is intentional. I may have designed the blocks and given you the instructions on what to cut and where to stitch, but I have not infused the blocks with any meaning. This is your quilt. The fabrics that you choose, the colors that you use and why you are making it are what will give the quilt a purpose. Name your blocks, write in the margins, cross out the ones you don't like, draw hearts around the ones that you love. In a perfect world, everyone's book would end up looking like a journal, coffee stains and all. The more adventurous ones might rename the book and write their own introduction. *Tula Pink's City Sampler* is a collaboration between you and me. I am the platform and you are the speaker, so stand on my shoulders and tell the future who you are and why you make.

In the end, it all comes down to this: Making something again is easy, making something new is brave and making something personal is essential.

Tula Pink

CHAPTER ONE

THE BLOCKS

Quilting is about using simple shapes to create new and more intricate shapes and patterns. This means that there are many ways to build a quilt block, and experimenting with the available options is half the fun. Each of the following sections will focus on a particular shape that you will use to build your blocks. This will allow you to explore a few of these infinite possibilities while keeping the piecing as simple as possible.

All blocks will measure 6½" (16.5cm) when unfinished and 6"(15.2cm) when finished.

Write your block name here

Write your fabric notes here

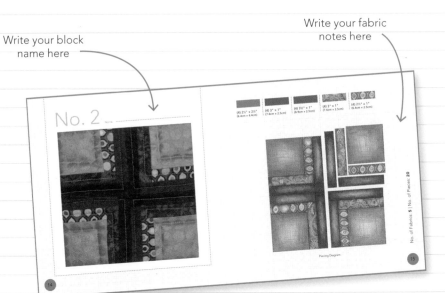

9

Blocks 1–15: Crosses

The cross divides a block both horizontally and vertically, giving us four large quarters and a strong center piece. The cross is the focus of the block. It will center the composition and balance a block quicker than any other shape. As dominant as this shape is, it still leaves a lot of space for interpretation. You can build a cross with a single fabric or break it down into smaller pieces. You can build it with any of the shapes from any of the following chapters, and this is why the cross block is a great way to start a quilt and get you warmed up for the rest of the blocks.

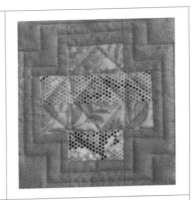

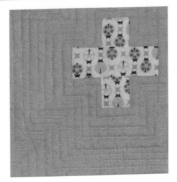

(4) 1½" × 1½"
(3.8cm × 3.8cm)

(4) 1½" × 2½"
(3.8cm × 6.4cm)

(4) 1½" × 3½"
(3.8cm × 8.9cm)

(4) 1½" × 2½"
(3.8cm × 6.4cm)

(4) 1½" × 1½"
(3.8cm × 3.8cm)

Piecing Diagram

No. of Fabrics: **4** | No. of Pieces: **20**

No. 2

(4) 2½" × 2½"
(6.4cm × 6.4cm)

(4) 3" × 1"
(7.6cm × 2.5cm)

(4) 3½" × 1"
(8.9cm × 2.5cm)

(4) 3" × 1"
(7.6cm × 2.5cm)

(4) 2½" × 1"
(6.4cm × 2.5cm)

Piecing Diagram

No. of Fabrics: **5** | No. of Pieces: **20**

15

No. 3

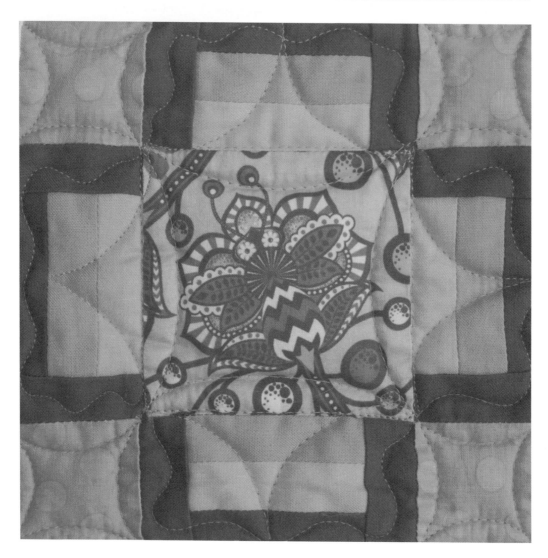

(8) 2" × 1"
(5.1cm × 2.5cm)

(1) 3½" × 3½"
(8.9cm × 8.9cm)

(4) 2½" × 1"
(6.4cm × 2.5cm)

(4) 2½" × 1"
(6.4cm × 2.5cm)

(4) 2" × 2"
(5.1cm × 5.1cm)

(4) 2½" × 1"
(6.4cm × 2.5cm)

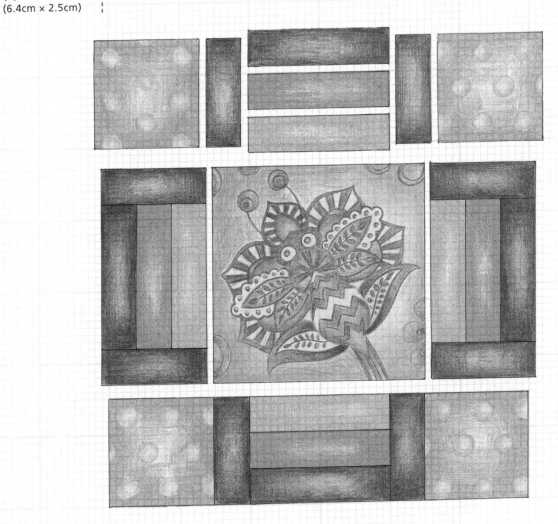

Piecing Diagram

No. of Fabrics: **5** | No. of Pieces: **25**

No. 4

Name: _____

(4) 1" × 2"
(2.5cm × 5.1cm)

(4) 1" × 2½"
(2.5cm × 6.4cm)

(4) 2" × 2"
(5.1cm × 5.1cm)

(4) 2½" × 1½"
(6.4cm × 3.8cm)

(4) 2½" × 1½"
(6.4cm × 3.8cm)

(1) 2½" × 2½"
(6.4cm × 6.4cm)

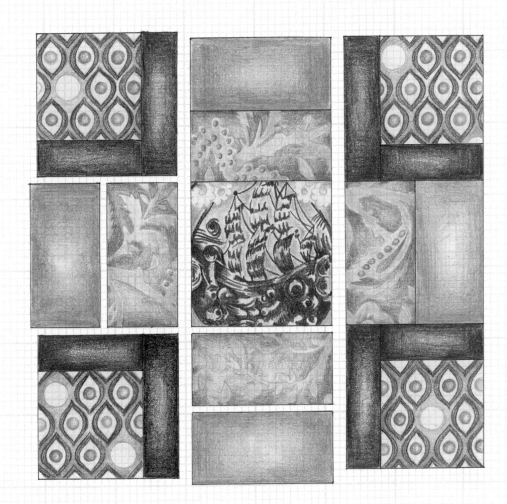

Piecing Diagram

No. of Fabrics: **5** | No. of Pieces: **21**

No. 5

(4) 2½" × 2½"
(6.4cm × 6.4cm)

 (2) 2½" × 1½"
(6.4cm × 3.8cm)

(1) 6½" × 1½"
(16.5cm × 3.8cm)

 (2) 2½" × 1½"
(6.4cm × 3.8cm)

(1) 6½" × 1½"
(16.5cm × 3.8cm)

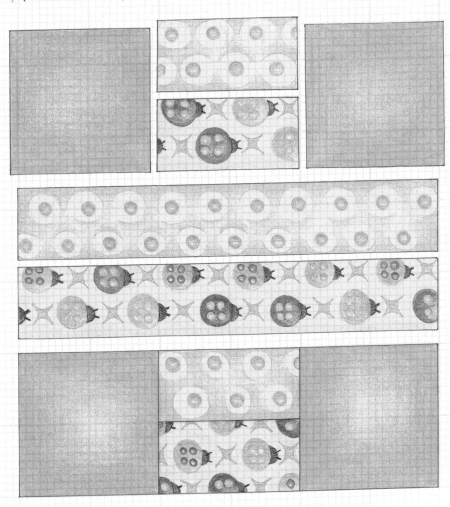

Piecing Diagram

No. of Fabrics: **3** | No. of Pieces: **10**

21

No. 6

Name: _____

 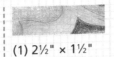

(1) 2½" × 1½"
(6.4cm × 3.8cm)

(4) 2½" × 2½"
(6.4cm × 6.4cm)

(1) 2½" × 1½"
(6.4cm × 3.8cm)

(1) 4½" × 1½"
(11.4cm × 3.8cm)

(4) 2½" × 1½"
(6.4cm × 3.8cm)

(1) 4½" × 1½"
(11.4cm × 3.8cm)

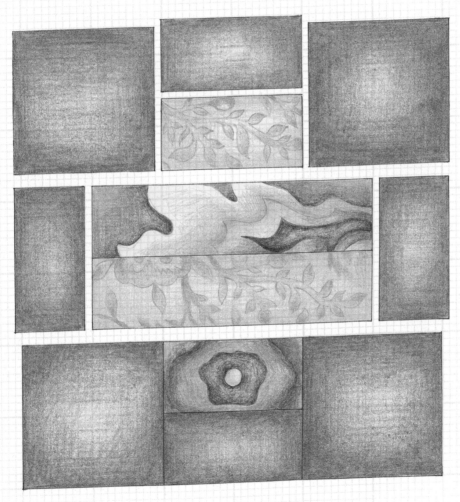

Piecing Diagram

No. of Fabrics: **3** | No. of Pieces: **12**

23

Name: _____

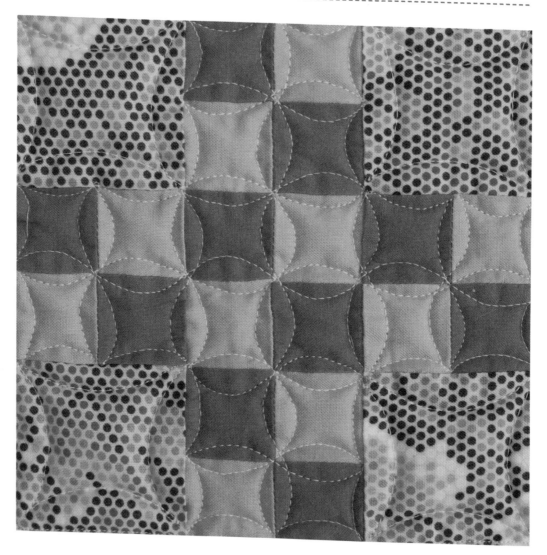

 **(4) 2½" × 2½"**
(6.4cm × 6.4cm)

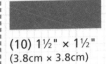 **(10) 1½" × 1½"**
(3.8cm × 3.8cm)

(10) 1½" × 1½"
(3.8cm × 3.8cm)

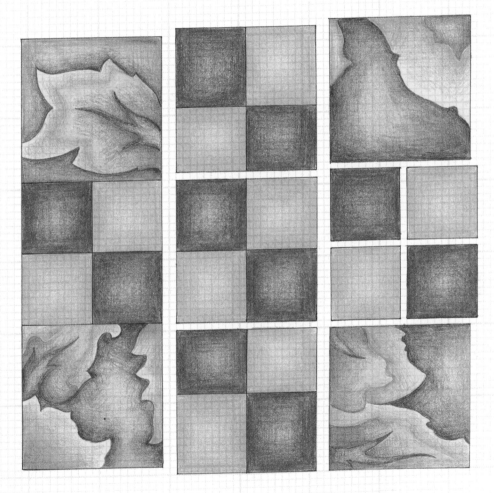

Piecing Diagram

No. of Fabrics: **3** | No. of Pieces: **24**

Name: _____

 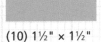

(2) 4½" × 1½"
(11.4cm × 3.8cm)

(6) 2½" × 1½"
(6.4cm × 3.8cm)

(10) 1½" × 1½"
(3.8cm × 3.8cm)

(6) 1½" × 1½"
(3.8cm × 3.8cm)

Piecing Diagram

No. of Fabrics: **3** | No. of Pieces: **24**

No. 9

(4) 2" × 2"
(5.1cm × 5.1cm)

(2) 3½" × 1½"
(8.9cm × 3.8cm)

(4) 3½" × 1"
(8.9cm × 2.5cm)

(1) 5½" × 3½"
(14cm × 8.9cm)

Piecing Diagram

No. of Fabrics: **2** | No. of Pieces: **11**

29

No. 10

(4) 2½" × 2½"
(6.4cm × 6.4cm)

(2) 2½" × 1½"
(6.4cm × 3.8cm)

(4) 1½" × 2½"
(3.8cm × 6.4cm)

(1) 4½" × 2½"
(11.4cm × 6.4cm)

Piecing Diagram

No. of Fabrics: **2** | No. of Pieces: **11**

31

(1) 5½" × 1"
(14cm × 2.5cm)

(4) 1" × 1"
(2.5cm × 2.5cm)

(2) 1" × 2¾"
(2.5cm × 7cm)

(4) 3¼" × 3¼"
(8.3cm × 8.3cm)

Piecing Diagram

No. of Fabrics: **2** | No. of Pieces: **11**

33

No. 12

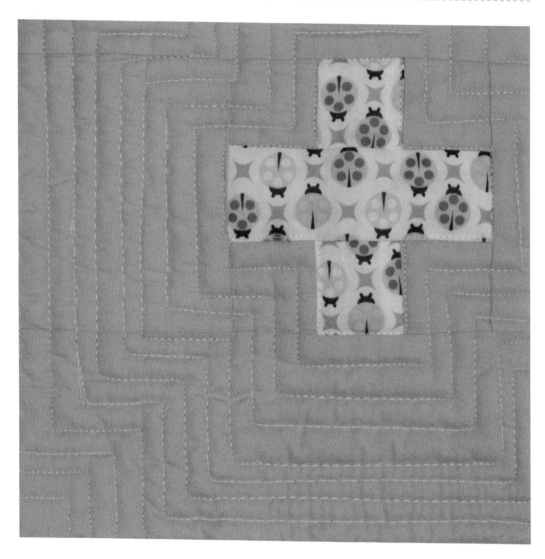

(1) 6½" × 1"
(16.5cm × 2.5cm)

(1) 6½" × 3"
(16.5cm × 7.6cm)

(4) 1½" × 1½"
(3.8cm × 3.8cm)

(2) 1½" × 1½"
(3.8cm × 3.8cm)

(1) 3" × 3½"
(7.6cm × 8.9cm)

(1) 1" × 3½"
(2.5cm × 8.9cm)

(1) 3½" × 1½"
(8.9cm × 3.8cm)

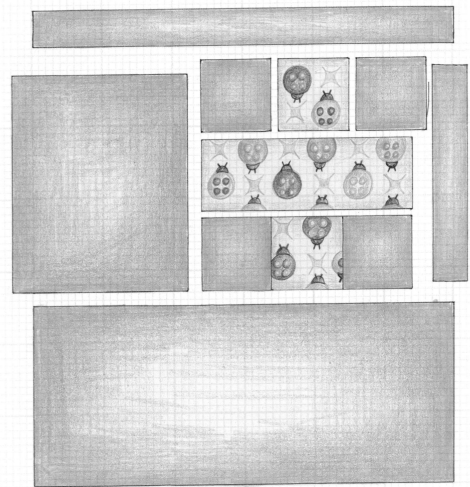

Piecing Diagram

No. of Fabrics: **2** | No. of Pieces: **11**

No. 13 Name: _____

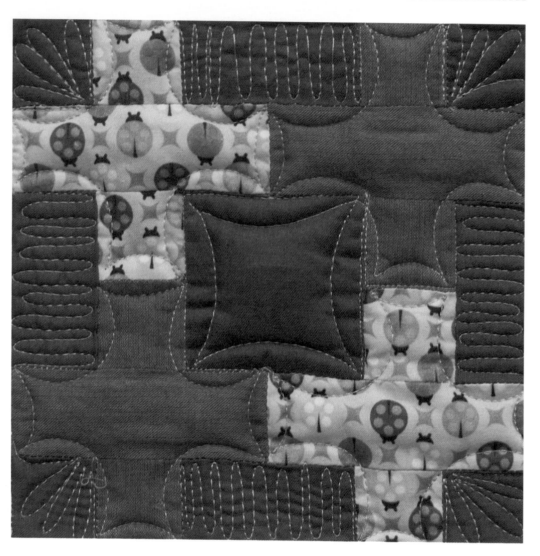

  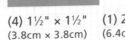

(4) 1½" × 1½"
(3.8cm × 3.8cm)

(4) 1½" × 1½"
(3.8cm × 3.8cm)

(4) 1½" × 1½"
(3.8cm × 3.8cm)

(1) 2½" × 2½"
(6.4cm × 6.4cm)

(2) 3½" × 1½"
(8.9cm × 3.8cm)

(2) 3½" × 1½"
(8.9cm × 3.8cm)

(4) 2½" × 1½"
(6.4cm × 3.8cm)

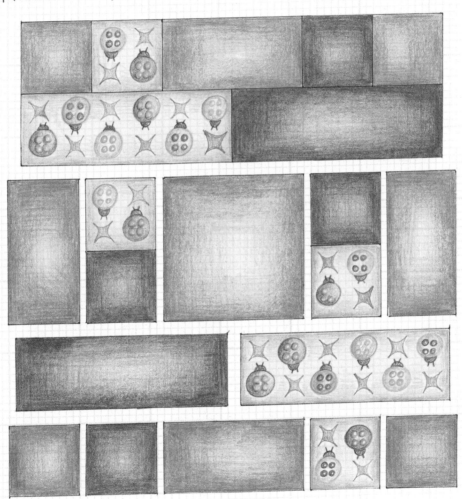

Piecing Diagram

No. of Fabrics: **3** | No. of Pieces: **21**

37

No. 14

Name: _____

(2) 1" × 3¼"
(2.5cm × 8.3cm)

(4) 1½" × 2¼"
(3.8cm × 5.7cm)

(4) 2¼" × 2¼"
(5.7cm × 5.7cm)

(1) 6½" × 1"
(16.5cm × 2.5cm)

(4) 1½" × 3¼"
(3.8cm × 8.3cm)

Piecing Diagram

No. of Fabrics: **3** | No. of Pieces: **15**

39

No. 15

Name: _____

(2) 6½" × 1"
(16.5cm × 2.5cm)

(2) 2½" × 2½"
(6.4cm × 6.4cm)

(4) 1½" × 1½"
(3.8cm × 3.8cm)

(2) 5½" × 1"
(14cm × 2.5cm)

(7) 1½" × 1½"
(3.8cm × 3.8cm)

(2) 3½" × 1½"
(8.9cm × 3.8cm)

Piecing Diagram

No. of Fabrics: **2** | No. of Pieces: **19**

Blocks 16–35: Rectangles

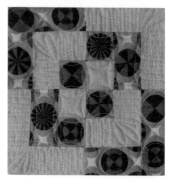

I love a perfectly symmetrical block, but I also love a block that does something a little unexpected. Setting a rectangle in a square block is the simplest way to add a little flavor. A rectangle, at its core, is simply a square with more personality. A square has four equal sides, and no matter which way you turn it, it will always look the same. A rectangle has more versatility—every time you turn a rectangle, you are dealing with a new possibility.

(2) 1" × 3½"
(2.5cm × 8.9cm)

(2) 1" × 3½"
(2.5cm × 8.9cm)

(2) 1" × 3½"
(2.5cm × 8.9cm)

(2) 1" × 3½"
(2.5cm × 8.9cm)

(1) 2½" × 3½"
(6.4cm × 8.9cm)

(1) 2½" × 3½"
(6.4cm × 8.9cm)

(1) 2½" × 3½"
(6.4cm × 8.9cm)

(1) 2½" × 3½"
(6.4cm × 8.9cm)

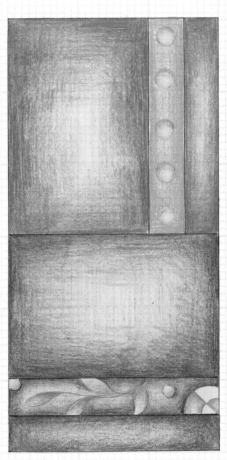

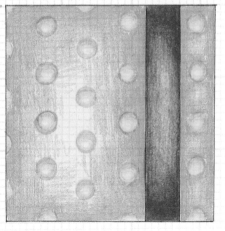

Piecing Diagram

No. of Fabrics: **4** | No. of Pieces: **12**

No. 17

Name: _____

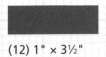

(12) 1" × 3½"
(2.5cm × 8.9cm)

(12) 1" × 3½"
(2.5cm × 8.9cm)

Piecing Diagram

No. of Fabrics: **2** | No. of Pieces: **24**

47

No. 18

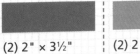 (2) 2" × 3½"
(5.1cm × 8.9cm)

 (2) 2" × 3½"
(5.1cm × 8.9cm)

(2) 2" × 3½"
(5.1cm × 8.9cm)

(2) 2" × 3½"
(5.1cm × 8.9cm)

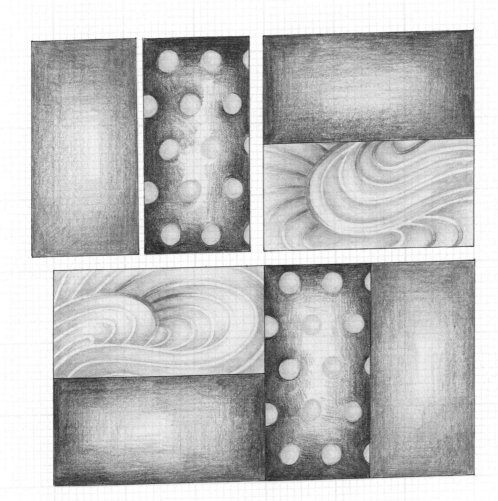

Piecing Diagram

No. of Fabrics: **4** | No. of Pieces: **8**

(2) 1½" × 2½"
(3.8cm × 6.4cm)

(2) 1" × 2½"
(2.5cm × 6.4cm)

(2) 1½" × 2½"
(3.8cm × 6.4cm)

(2) 1" × 2½"
(2.5cm × 6.4cm)

(2) 2" × 2½"
(5.1cm × 6.4cm)

(4) 3½" × 1"
(8.9cm × 2.5cm)

(2) 2" × 2½"
(5.1cm × 6.4cm)

(4) 3½" × 1"
(8.9cm × 2.5cm)

Piecing Diagram

No. of Fabrics: **2** | No. of Pieces: **20**

51

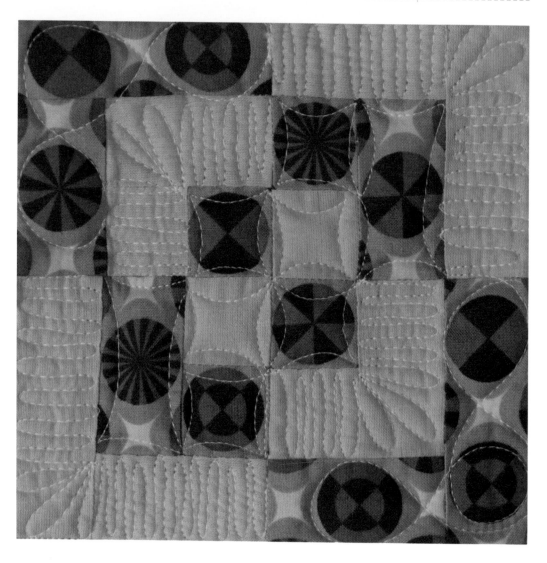

(4) 1½" × 1½"
(3.8cm × 3.8cm)

(2) 1½" × 3½"
(3.8cm × 8.9cm)

(4) 1½" × 2½"
(3.8cm × 6.4cm)

(4) 1½" × 1½"
(3.8cm × 3.8cm)

(2) 1½" × 3½"
(3.8cm × 8.9cm)

(4) 1½" × 2½"
(3.8cm × 6.4cm)

Piecing Diagram

No. of Fabrics: **2** | No. of Pieces: **20**

53

No. 21

(1) 6½" × 4½"
(16.5cm × 11.4cm)

(1) 1½" × 2½"
(3.8cm × 6.4cm)

(1) 3½" × 1½"
(8.9cm × 3.8cm)

(1) 2½" × 2½"
(6.4cm × 6.4cm)

(1) 3½" × 1½"
(8.9cm × 3.8cm)

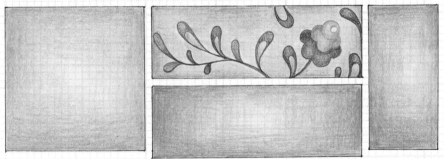

Piecing Diagram

Name: _____

(2) 3½" × 1½"
(8.9cm × 3.8cm)

(2) 3½" × 2½"
(8.9cm × 6.4cm)

(2) 3½" × 1½"
(8.9cm × 3.8cm)

(2) 3½" × 2½"
(8.9cm × 6.4cm)

Piecing Diagram

No. of Fabrics: **2** | No. of Pieces: **8**

(2) 6½" × 1½"
(16.5cm × 3.8cm)

(3) 2½" × 2½"
(6.4cm × 6.4cm)

(3) 2½" × 2½"
(6.4cm × 6.4cm)

Piecing Diagram

No. of Fabrics: **3** | No. of Pieces: **8**

59

Name: _____

(2) 1½" × 1½"
(3.8cm × 3.8cm)

(5) 1½" × 2½"
(3.8cm × 6.4cm)

(2) 1½" × 1½"
(3.8cm × 3.8cm)

(5) 1½" × 2½"
(3.8cm × 6.4cm)

(2) 1½" × 1½"
(3.8cm × 3.8cm)

(5) 1½" × 2½"
(3.8cm × 6.4cm)

Piecing Diagram

No. of Fabrics: **3** | No. of Pieces: **21**

No. 25

(1) 3½" × 2½"
(8.9cm × 6.4cm)

(3) 2½" × 1½"
(6.4cm × 3.8cm)

(1) 3½" × 2½"
(8.9cm × 6.4cm)

(3) 2½" × 1½"
(6.4cm × 3.8cm)

(1) 3½" × 2½"
(8.9cm × 6.4cm)

(3) 2½" × 1½"
(6.4cm × 3.8cm)

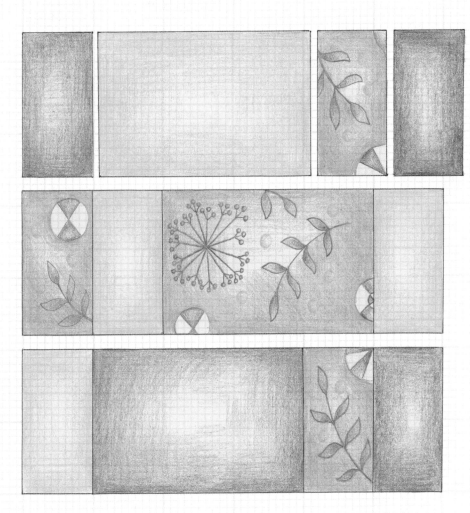

Piecing Diagram

No. of Fabrics: **3** | No. of Pieces: **12**

No. 26

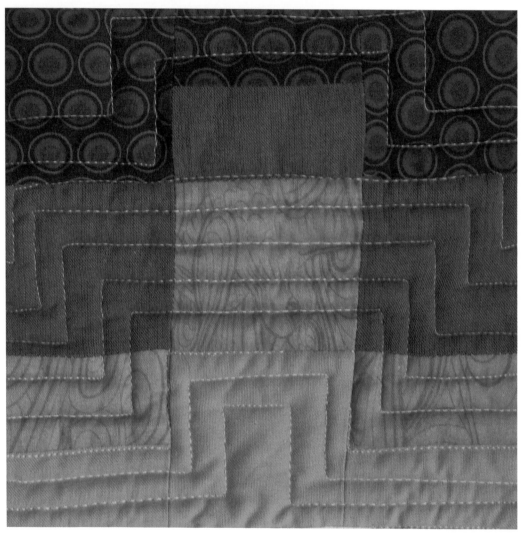

 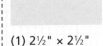 

(2) 2½" × 2½"
(6.4cm × 6.4cm)

(1) 1½" × 2½"
(3.8cm × 2.5cm)

(1) 2½" × 2½"
(6.4cm × 6.4cm)

(2) 1½" × 2½"
(3.8cm × 6.4cm)

(1) 1½" × 2½"
(3.8cm × 6.4cm)

(2) 2½" × 2½"
(6.4cm × 6.4cm)

(2) 1½" × 2½"
(3.8cm × 6.4cm)

(1) 2½" × 2½"
(6.4cm × 6.4cm)

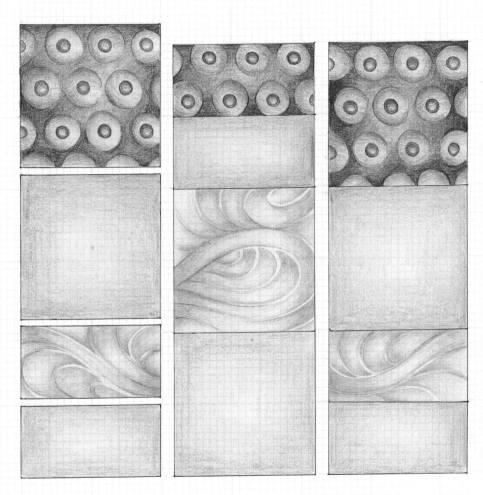

Piecing Diagram

No. of Fabrics: **4** | No. of Pieces: **12**

No. 27

Name: _____

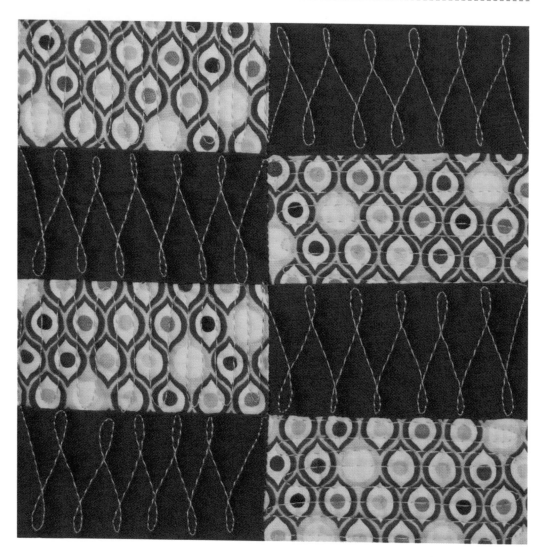

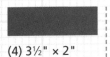

(4) 3½" × 2"
(8.9cm × 5.1cm)

(4) 3½" × 2"
(8.9cm × 5.1cm)

Piecing Diagram

No. of Fabrics: **2** | No. of Pieces: **8**

(1) 3½" × 3½"
(8.9cm × 8.9cm)

(1) 3½" × 2½"
(8.9cm × 6.4cm)

(1) 3½" × 3½"
(8.9cm × 8.9cm)

(1) 3½" × 2½"
(8.9cm × 6.4cm)

(1) 3½" × 1½"
(8.9cm × 3.8cm)

(1) 1½" × 1½"
(3.8cm × 3.8cm)

(1) 2½" × 1½"
(6.4cm × 3.8cm)

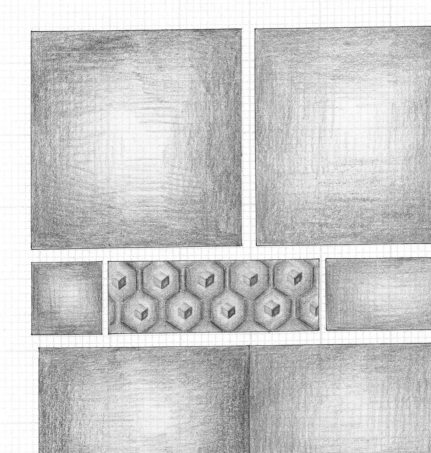

Piecing Diagram

No. 29

(2) 3½" × 1"
(8.9cm × 2.5cm)

(2) 4½" × 1"
(11.4cm × 2.5cm)

(1) 3½" × 2½"
(8.9cm × 6.4cm)

(1) 3½" × 2½"
(8.9cm × 6.4cm)

(2) 1" × 5½"
(2.5cm × 14cm)

(2) 1½" × 6½"
(3.8cm × 16.5cm)

Piecing Diagram

No. of Fabrics: **4** | No. of Pieces: **10**

No. 30

Name: _____

(2) 6½" × 1½"
(16.5cm × 3.8cm)

(6) 1" × 2½"
(2.5cm × 6.4cm)

(6) 1" × 2½"
(2.5cm × 6.4cm)

(2) 2" × 4½"
(5.1cm × 11.4cm)

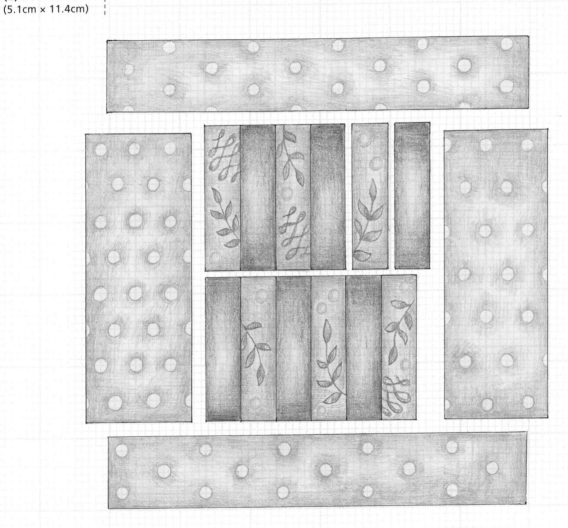

Piecing Diagram

No. of Fabrics: **3** | No. of Pieces: **16**

73

No. 31

Name:

(1) 3½" × 1"
(8.9cm × 2.5cm)

(2) 1" × 5½"
(2.5cm × 14cm)

(2) 4½" × 1"
(11.4cm × 2.5cm)

(4) 1½" × 1½"
(3.8cm × 3.8cm)

(5) 1½" × 1½"
(3.8cm × 3.8cm)

(1) 3½" × 2"
(8.9cm × 5.1cm)

(2) 1½" × 6½"
(3.8cm × 16.5cm)

Piecing Diagram

No. of Fabrics: **4** | No. of Pieces: **17**

No. 32

(2) 3½" × 1"
(8.9cm × 2.5cm)

(2) 4½" × 1"
(11.4cm × 2.5cm)

(2) 6½" × 1"
(16.5cm × 2.5cm)

(1) 1" × 5½"
(2.5cm × 14cm)

(1) 3" × 1½"
(7.6cm × 3.8cm)

(1) 3" × 2½"
(7.6cm × 6.4cm)

(1) 3" × 2½"
(7.6cm × 6.4cm)

(1) 2½" × 4½"
(6.4cm × 11.4cm)

Piecing Diagram

No. 33

(1) 2½" × 4½"
(6.4cm × 11.4cm)

(1) 3½" × 4½"
(8.9cm × 11.4cm)

(1) 2½" × 2½"
(6.4cm × 6.4cm)

(1) 4½" × 2½"
(11.4cm × 6.4cm)

(1) 1½" × 4½"
(3.8cm × 11.4cm)

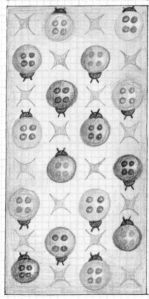

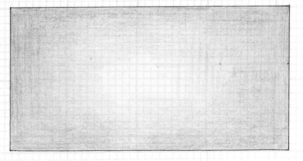

Piecing Diagram

No. of Fabrics: **3** | No. of Pieces: **5**

No. 34

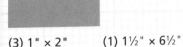  

(3) 1" × 2"
(2.5cm × 5.1cm)

(1) 1½" × 6½"
(3.8cm × 16.5cm)

(1) 4" × 4"
(10.2cm × 10.2cm)

(2) 1" × 1"
(2.5cm × 2.5cm)

(1) 1½" × 2½"
(3.8cm × 6.4cm)

(1) 5½" × 1"
(14cm × 2.5cm)

(1) 1½" × 4"
(3.8cm × 10.2cm)

(1) 4" × 2½"
(10.2cm × 6.4cm)

Piecing Diagram

No. of Fabrics: **3** | No. of Pieces: **11**

81

(1) 1½" × 4½"
(3.8cm × 11.4cm)

(3) 1½" × 2½"
(3.8cm × 6.4cm)

(2) 1½" × 4½"
(3.8cm × 11.4cm)

(1) 3½" × 4½"
(8.9cm × 11.4cm)

(3) 1½" × 2½"
(3.8cm × 6.4cm)

Piecing Diagram

No. of Fabrics: **2** | No. of Pieces: **10**

Blocks 36–55: Triangles

The quickest way to add interest to a block is with a triangle. Triangles make pinwheels and sawtooth patterns, zigzags and chevrons among other things. The possibilities that a triangle brings to piecing are endless. This section attempts to explore a few of those possibilities.

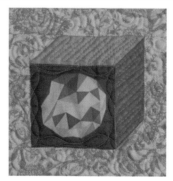

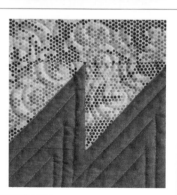

Before You Begin

METHOD 1: Half Square Triangle

Any time you see this ◨ symbol, follow these instructions:

This symbol will always show up in a pair of identical size squares from two different fabrics that will go together to make one half square triangle.

1. Draw a diagonal line from the upper right corner to the lower left corner on the *wrong* side of one of your squares.

2. Place your two squares right sides together and sew ON the drawn line.

3. Trim away the excess leaving a ¼" (6mm) seam allowance on one side of the stitched line.

4. Press your seams open.

5. Repeat until all fabrics containing that symbol have been made into half square triangles.

METHOD 1 blocks: 36, 37, 38, 45, 46, 47, 48, 50, 52, 55

METHOD 2: Cutting Corners

Any time you see this ◲ symbol, follow these instructions:

This symbol is used when you are attaching a half square triangle to the corner of a larger square or rectangle.

1. Draw a diagonal line from the upper right corner to the lower left corner on the *wrong* side of your square.

2. Use the block diagram to determine the placement of the triangle on the larger piece.

3. Line up your square with the edges of the larger piece (right sides together) so that the drawn line is facing up.

4. Sew on the drawn line.

5. Trim away the excess fabric leaving a ¼" (6mm) seam allowance on the outside of the stitched line.

6. Press seams open.

METHOD 2 blocks: 39, 40, 49

METHOD 3: Flying Geese

Any time you see this ◺◻ symbol, follow these instructions:

This symbol is used when creating flying geese. To create the flying geese, you will use method 2 on opposite corners of the same base rectangle.

METHOD 3 blocks: 41, 42, 43, 44, 51, 53, 54

 (1) 6½" × 2½"
(16.5cm × 6.4cm)

(1) 1½" × 3½"
(3.8cm × 8.9cm)

 (1) 3½" × 3½" ☑
(8.9cm × 8.9cm)

 (1) 3½" × 3½" ☑
(8.9cm × 8.9cm)

(1) 2½" × 3½"
(6.4cm × 8.9cm)

(1) 6½" × 1½"
(16.5cm × 3.8cm)

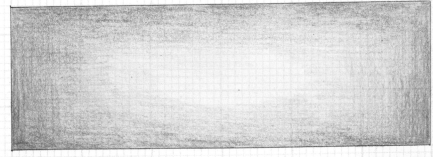

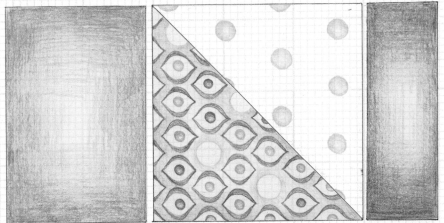

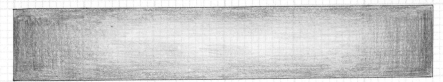

Piecing Diagram

No. 37

Name: _____

(2) 6½" × 1½"
(16.5cm × 3.8cm)

(1) 4½" × 4½" ☑
(11.4cm × 11.4cm)

(1) 4½" × 4½" ☑
(11.4cm × 11.4cm)

(2) 1½" × 4½"
(3.8cm × 11.4cm)

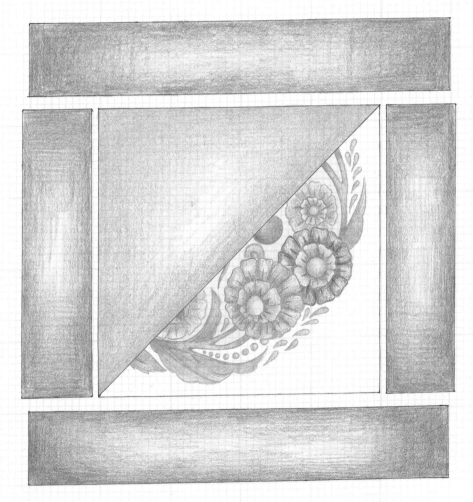

Piecing Diagram

No. of Fabrics: **3** | No. of Pieces: **6**

(1) 6½" × 2"
(16.5cm × 5.1cm)

(1) 6½" × 2"
(16.5cm × 5.1cm)

(2) 3½" × 3½" ◻
(8.9cm × 8.9cm)

(2) 3½" × 3½" ◻
(8.9cm × 8.9cm)

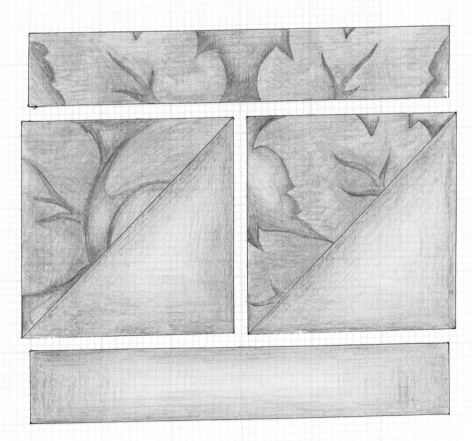

Piecing Diagram

No. of Fabrics: **2** | No. of Pieces: **6**

 (2) 6½" × 1½"
(16.5cm × 3.8cm)

(2) 1½" × 4½"
(3.8cm × 11.4cm)

 (2) 1½" × 1½"
(3.8cm × 3.8cm)

 (1) 1½" × 4½"
(3.8cm × 11.4cm)

(1) 3½" × 1½"
(8.9cm × 3.8cm)

(1) 1½" × 1½"
(3.8cm × 3.8cm)

 (1) 3½" × 3½"
(8.9cm × 8.9cm)

Piecing Diagram

No. of Fabrics: **4** | No. of Pieces: **10**

93

No. 40

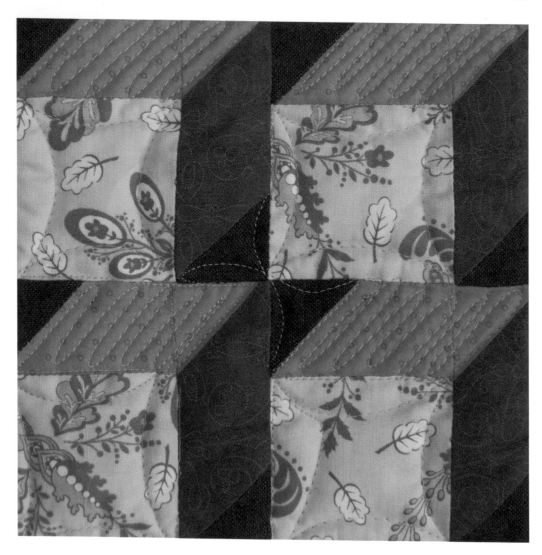

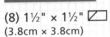

(8) 1½" × 1½" ⬜
(3.8cm × 3.8cm)

(4) 1½" × 3½"
(3.8cm × 8.9cm)

(4) 2½" × 1½"
(6.4cm × 3.8cm)

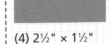

(4) 1½" × 1½" ⬜
(3.8cm × 3.8cm)

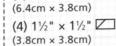

(4) 2½" × 2½"
(6.4cm × 6.4cm)

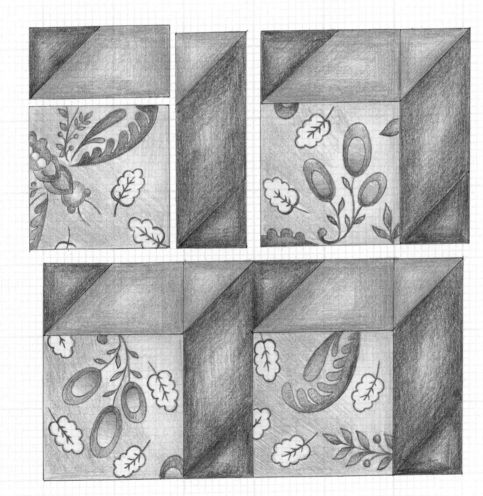

Piecing Diagram

No. of Fabrics: **4** | No. of Pieces: **24**

(2) 3½" × 5"
(8.9cm × 12.7cm)

(2) 3½" × 2"
(8.9cm × 5.1cm)

(4) 2" × 2" ◹
(5.1cm × 5.1cm)

(4) 2" × 2" ◺
(5.1cm × 5.1cm)

Piecing Diagram

No. of Fabrics: **3** | No. of Pieces: **12**

97

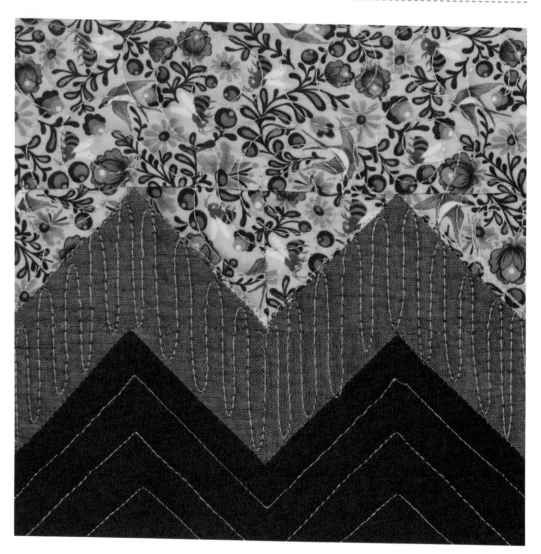

(1) 6½" × 1½"
(16.5cm × 3.8cm)

(2) 3½" × 2"
(8.9cm × 5.1cm)

(2) 3½" × 2"
(8.9cm × 5.1cm)

(4) 2" × 2" ⬜
(5.1cm × 5.1cm)

(1) 6½" × 2½"
(16.5cm × 6.4cm)

(4) 2" × 2" ⬜
(5.1cm × 5.1cm)

Piecing Diagram

No. 43

(1) 1½" × 6½"
(3.8cm × 16.5cm)

(2) 3½" × 2"
(8.9cm × 5.1cm)

(2) 3½" × 2"
(8.9cm × 5.1cm)

(1) 2½" × 6½"
(6.4cm × 16.5cm)

(4) 2" × 2" ◺
(5.1cm × 5.1cm)

(4) 2" × 2" ◺
(5.1cm × 5.1cm)

Piecing Diagram

No. of Fabrics: **3** | No. of Pieces: **14**

No. 44

Name: _____

(1) 6½" × 3½"
(16.5cm × 8.9cm)

(2) 3½" × 3½"
(8.9cm × 8.9cm)

(1) 6½" × 3½"
(16.5cm × 8.9cm)

(2) 3½" × 3½"
(8.9cm × 8.9cm)

Piecing Diagram

No. of Fabrics: **2** | No. of Pieces: **6**

103

No. 45

Name: _____

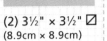

(2) 3½" × 3½" ☑
(8.9cm × 8.9cm)

(2) 3½" × 3½" ☑
(8.9cm × 8.9cm)

(2) 3½" × 3½" ☑
(8.9cm × 8.9cm)

(2) 3½" × 3½" ☑
(8.9cm × 8.9cm)

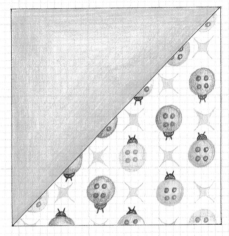  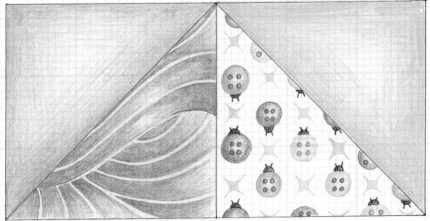

Piecing Diagram

No. of Fabrics: **4** | No. of Pieces: **8**

No. 46

Name: _____

 **(4)** 3½" × 3½" ☑
(8.9cm × 8.9cm)

(4) 3½" × 3½" ☑
(8.9cm × 8.9cm)

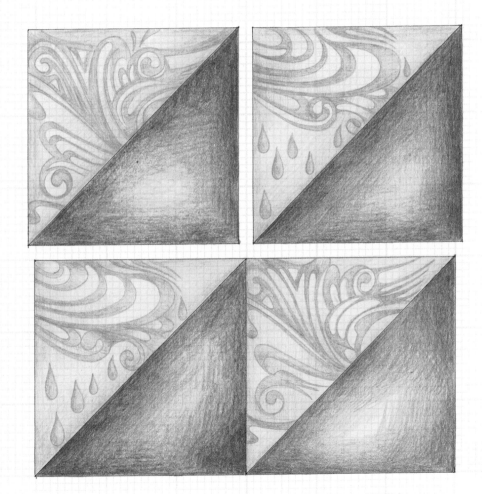

Piecing Diagram

No. of Fabrics: **2** | No. of Pieces: **8**

107

No. 47

Name: _____

(9) 2½" × 2½" ☒
(6.4cm × 6.4cm)

(9) 2½" × 2½" ☒
(6.4cm × 6.4cm)

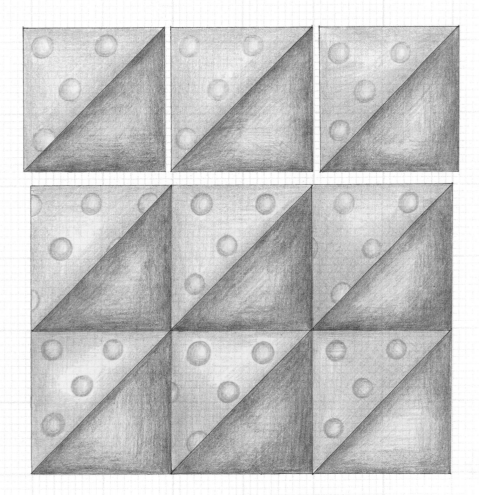

Piecing Diagram

No. of Fabrics: **2** | No. of Pieces: **18**

109

No. 48

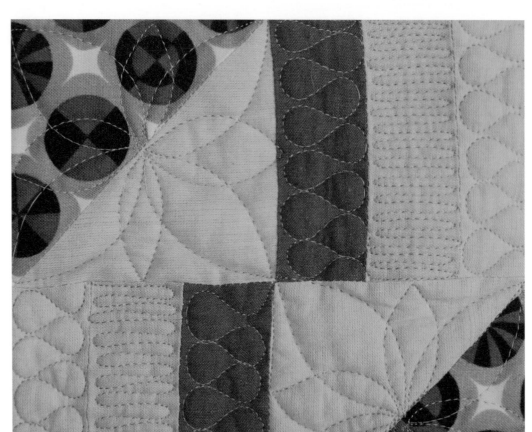

 (2) 3½" × 3½" ☑
(8.9cm × 8.9cm)

 (2) 1½" × 3½"
(3.8cm × 8.9cm)

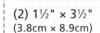 (2) 1½" × 3½"
(3.8cm × 8.9cm)

(2) 1½" × 3½"
(3.8cm × 8.9cm)

(2) 3½" × 3½" ☑
(8.9cm × 8.9cm)

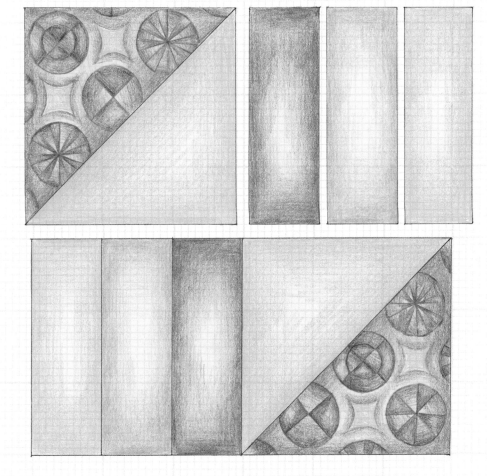

Piecing Diagram

No. of Fabrics: **4** | No. of Pieces: **10**

111

No. 49

Name: _____

 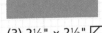

(1) 6½" × 2½"
(16.5cm × 6.4cm)

(2) 4½" × 2½"
(11.4cm × 6.4cm)

(3) 2½" × 2½"
(6.4cm × 6.4cm)

(1) 2½" × 2½"
(6.4cm × 6.4cm)

(1) 2½" × 2½" ☑
(6.4cm × 6.4cm)

Piecing Diagram

No. of Fabrics: **2** | No. of Pieces: **8**

No. 50

Name: _____

(2) 6½" × 1"
(16.5cm × 2.5cm)

(2) 1½" × 5½"
(3.8cm × 14cm)

(9) 1½" × 1½" ☑
(3.8cm × 3.8cm)

(9) 1½" × 1½" ☑
(3.8cm × 3.8cm)

(2) 1" × 5½"
(2.5cm × 14cm)

(6) 1½" × 1½"
(3.8cm × 3.8cm)

Piecing Diagram

No. of Fabrics: **3** | No. of Pieces: **30**

115

No. 51

(4) 3½" × 2"
(8.9cm × 5.1cm)

(8) 2" × 2"
(5.1cm × 5.1cm)

(4) 3½" × 2"
(8.9cm × 5.1cm)

(8) 2" × 2"
(5.1cm × 5.1cm)

Piecing Diagram

No. of Fabrics: **2** | No. of Pieces: **24**

(1) 4½" × 2½"
(11.4cm × 6.4cm)

(3) 2½" × 2½" ☑
(6.4cm × 6.4cm)

(1) 2½" × 2½"
(6.4cm × 6.4cm)

(1) 4½" × 2½"
(11.4cm × 6.4cm)

(3) 2½" × 2½" ☑
(6.4cm × 6.4cm)

(1) 2½" × 2½"
(6.4cm × 6.4cm)

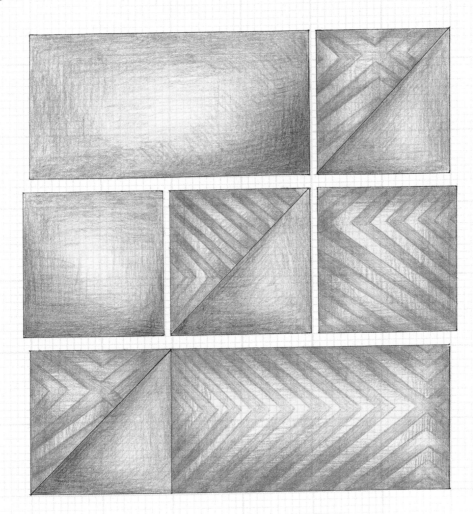

Piecing Diagram

No. of Fabrics: **2** | No. of Pieces: **10**

119

 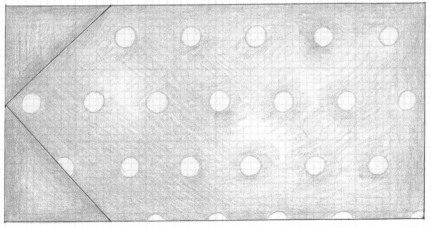

(4) 2" × 2" ▱
(5.1cm × 5.1cm)

(1) 6½" × 3½"
(16.5cm × 8.9cm)

(1) 6½" × 3½"
(16.5cm × 8.9cm)

Piecing Diagram

No. of Fabrics: **3** | No. of Pieces: **6**

121

No. 54

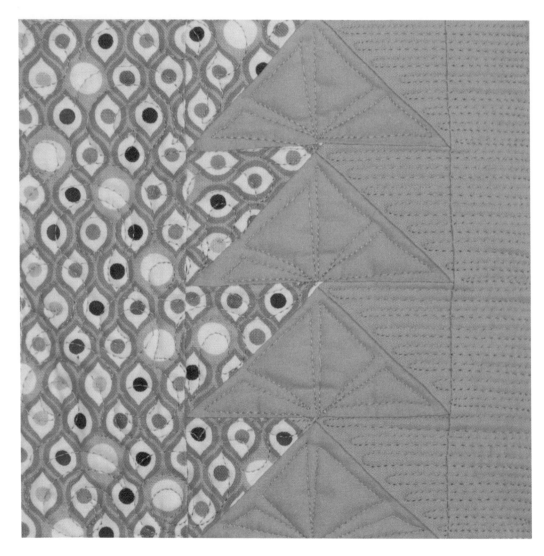

(1) 2½" × 6½"
(6.4cm × 16.5cm)

(1) 1½" × 6½"
(3.8cm × 16.5cm)

(4) 3½" × 2"
(8.9cm × 5.1cm)

(4) 2" × 2" ⊠
(5.1cm × 5.1cm)

(4) 2" × 2" ⊠
(5.1cm × 5.1cm)

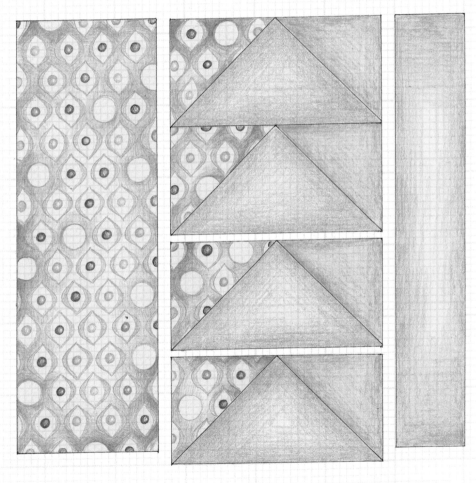

Piecing Diagram

No. of Fabrics: **3** | No. of Pieces: **14**

123

No. 55

(9) 2½" × 2½" ☑
(6.4cm × 6.4cm)

(9) 2½" × 2½" ☑
(6.4cm × 6.4cm)

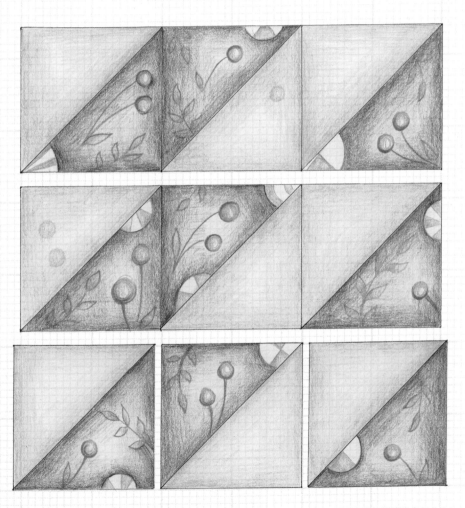

Piecing Diagram

No. of Fabrics: **2** | No. of Pieces: **18**

125

Blocks 56–70: Stripes

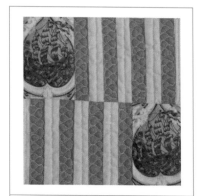

A stripe is a pattern in and of itself. When translating a stripe into a 6" (15.2cm) block, we have the opportunity to use our fabrics to create new textures and patterns. The stripe is both classic and modern, staid and playful, but always bold.

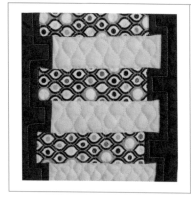

No. 56

Name: _____

(2) 1½" × 6½"
(3.8cm × 16.5cm)

(2) 3½" × 2"
(8.9cm × 5.1cm)

(1) 1½" × 6½"
(3.8cm × 16.5cm)

(2) 3½" × 2"
(8.9cm × 5.1cm)

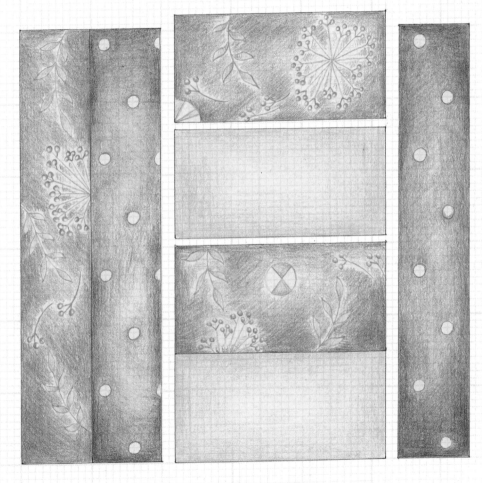

Piecing Diagram

No. of Fabrics: **3** | No. of Pieces: **7**

Name: _____

(1) 1½" × 1½"
(3.8cm × 3.8cm)

(2) 4½" × 1½"
(11.4cm × 3.8cm)

(1) 2½" × 1½"
(6.4cm × 3.8cm)

(3) 4½" × 1½"
(11.4cm × 3.8cm)

(1) 2½" × 6½"
(6.4cm × 16.5cm)

(1) 1½" × 1½"
(3.8cm × 3.8cm)

Piecing Diagram

No. of Fabrics: **3** | No. of Pieces: **9**

131

No. 58

Name: _____

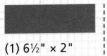 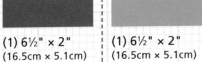  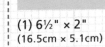

(1) 6½" × 2"
(16.5cm × 5.1cm)

(1) 6½" × 2"
(16.5cm × 5.1cm)

(1) 6½" × 2"
(16.5cm × 5.1cm)

(1) 6½" × 2"
(16.5cm × 5.1cm)

Piecing Diagram

No. of Fabrics: **4** | No. of Pieces: **4**

(3) 4½" × 1½"
(11.4cm × 3.8cm)

(3) 4½" × 1½"
(11.4cm × 3.8cm)

(6) 1½" × 1½"
(3.8cm × 3.8cm)

(6) 1½" × 1½"
(3.8cm × 3.8cm)

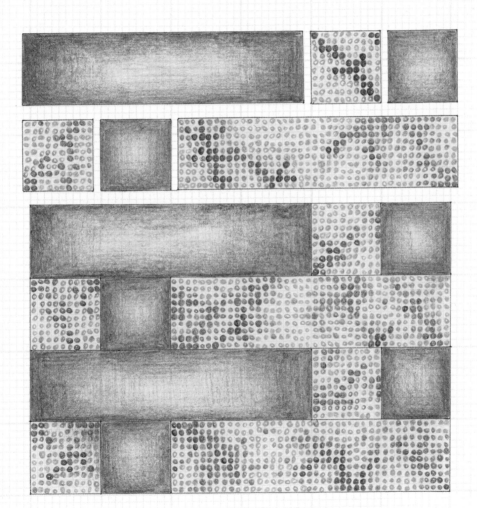

Piecing Diagram

No. of Fabrics: **2** | No. of Pieces: **18**

No. 60

(1) 1" × 6½"
(2.5cm × 16.5cm)

(1) 1½" × 1½"
(3.8cm × 3.8cm)

(1) 2" × 6½"
(5.1cm × 16.5cm)

(1) 2½" × 3½"
(6.4cm × 8.9cm)

(1) 1½" × 1½"
(3.8cm × 3.8cm)

(1) 2½" × 2½"
(6.4cm × 6.4cm)

(1) 1½" × 4½"
(3.8cm × 11.4cm)

(1) 2½" × 1½"
(6.4cm × 3.8cm)

(1) 1½" × 6½"
(3.8cm × 16.5cm)

Piecing Diagram

No. of Fabrics: **2** | No. of Pieces: **9**

(1) 6½" × 2½"
(16.5cm × 6.4cm)

(2) 6½" × 1½"
(16.5cm × 3.8cm)

(1) 3½" × 1½"
(8.9cm × 3.8cm)

(1) 1½" × 1½"
(3.8cm × 3.8cm)

(1) 6½" × 1½"
(16.5cm × 3.8cm)

(1) 2½" × 1½"
(6.4cm × 3.8cm)

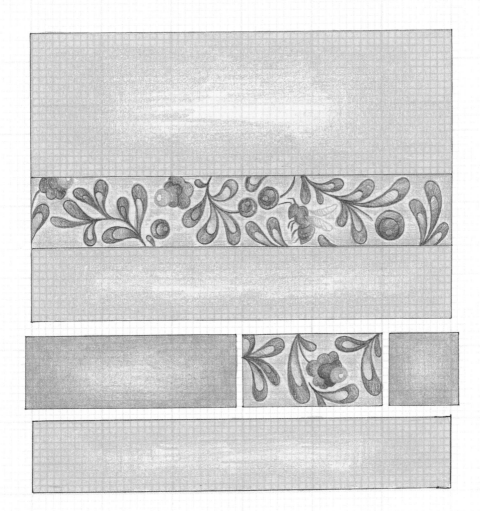

Piecing Diagram

No. of Fabrics: **3** | No. of Pieces: **7**

No. 62

Name: _____

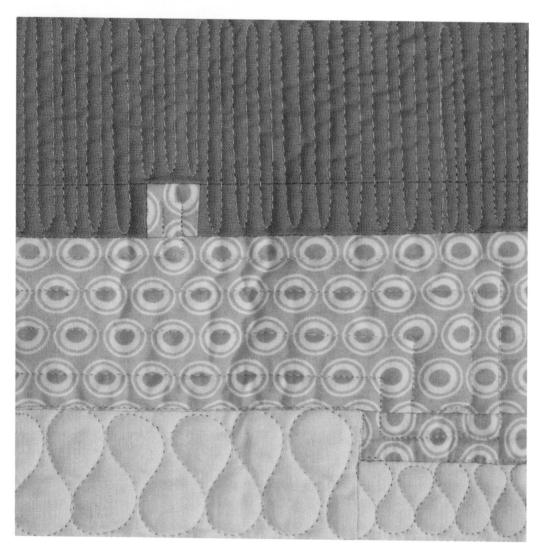

(1) 6½" × 2½"
(16.5cm × 6.4cm)

(1) 4½" × 1"
(11.4cm × 2.5cm)

(1) 1" × 1"
(2.5cm × 2.5cm)

(1) 2½" × 1"
(6.4cm × 2.5cm)

(1) 4½" × 2"
(11.4cm × 5.1cm)

(1) 2" × 1"
(5.1cm × 2.5cm)

(1) 6½" × 2½"
(16.5cm × 6.4cm)

(1) 2½" × 1½"
(6.4cm × 3.8cm)

Piecing Diagram

No. of Fabrics: **3** | No. of Pieces: **8**

Name: _____

(2) 6½" × 2"
(16.5cm × 5.1cm)

(2) 2½" × 1½"
(6.4cm × 3.8cm)

(2) 2½" × 1½"
(6.4cm × 3.8cm)

(2) 2½" × 1½"
(6.4cm × 3.8cm)

(1) 6½" × 1½"
(16.5cm × 3.8cm)

Piecing Diagram

No. of Fabrics: **4** | No. of Pieces: **9**

143

Name: _____

(2) 1½" × 1½"
(3.8cm × 3.8cm)

(2) 1½" × 3½"
(3.8cm × 8.9cm)

(1) 1½" × 3½"
(3.8cm × 8.9cm)

(1) 1½" × 5½"
(3.8cm × 14cm)

(1) 1½" × 3½"
(3.8cm × 8.9cm)

(1) 1½" × 5½"
(3.8cm × 14cm)

(2) 1½" × 2½"
(3.8cm × 6.4cm)

(1) 1½" × 4½"
(3.8cm × 11.4cm)

(1) 1½" × 4½"
(3.8cm × 11.4cm)

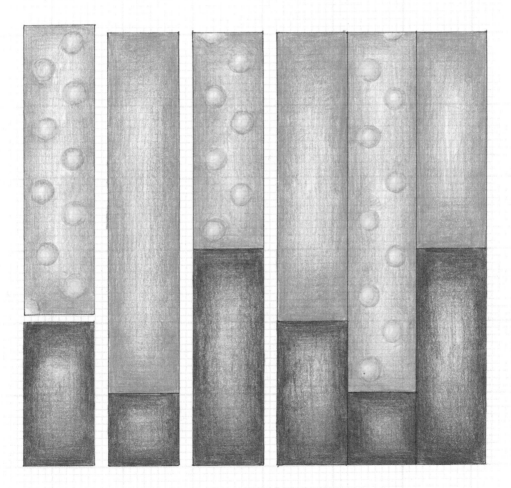

Piecing Diagram

No. of Fabrics: **3** | No. of Pieces: **12**

Name: _____

(2) 1½" × 6½" **(4)** 1½" × 2½"   **(2)** 1½" × 3½"   **(2)** 1½" × 3½"
(3.8cm × 16.5cm)   (3.8cm × 6.4cm)   (3.8cm × 8.9cm)   (3.8cm × 8.9cm)

(4) 1½" × 1½"
(3.8cm × 3.8cm)

Piecing Diagram

No. of Fabrics: **3** | No. of Pieces: **14**

147

No. 66

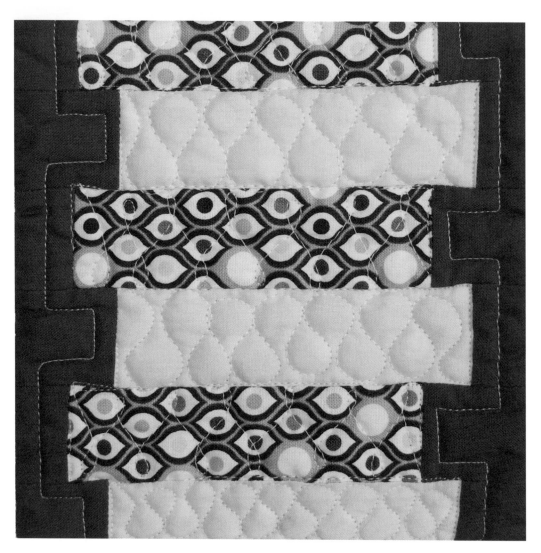

(6) 2" × 1½"
(5.1cm × 3.8cm)

(3) 4" × 1½"
(10.2cm × 3.8cm)

(3) 4" × 1½"
(10.2cm × 3.8cm)

(6) 1½" × 1½"
(3.8cm × 3.8cm)

Piecing Diagram

No. of Fabrics: **3** | No. of Pieces: **18**

No. 67

(2) 1" × 3½"
(2.5cm × 8.9cm)

(1) 1½" × 3½"
(3.8cm × 8.9cm)

(1) 6½" × 3½"
(16.5cm × 8.9cm)

(2) 1" × 3½"
(2.5cm × 8.9cm)

(1) 2½" × 3½"
(6.4cm × 8.9cm)

(1) 1½" × 3½"
(3.8cm × 8.9cm)

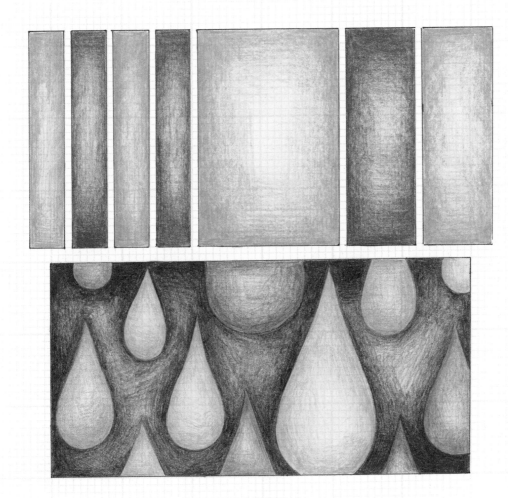

Piecing Diagram

No. 68

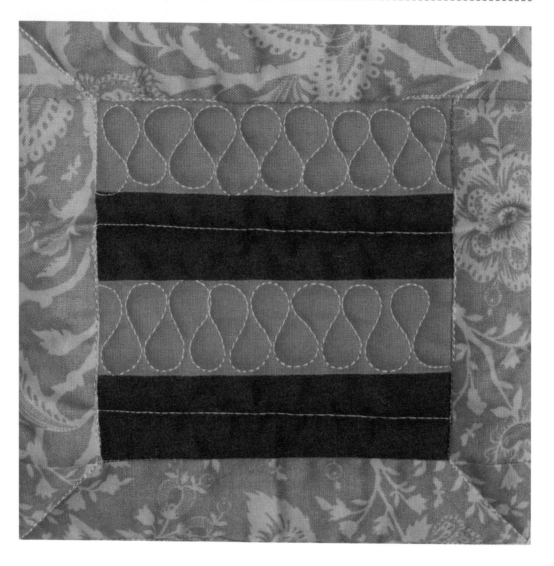

 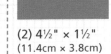

(2) 4½" × 1½"
(11.4cm × 3.8cm)

(2) 4½" × 1½"
(11.4cm × 3.8cm)

(2) 6½" × 1½"
(16.5cm × 3.8cm)

(2) 1½" × 4½"
(3.8cm × 11.4cm)

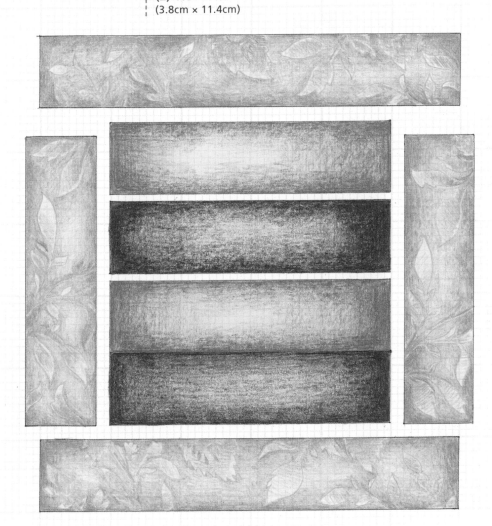

Piecing Diagram

No. of Fabrics: **3** | No. of Pieces: **8**

153

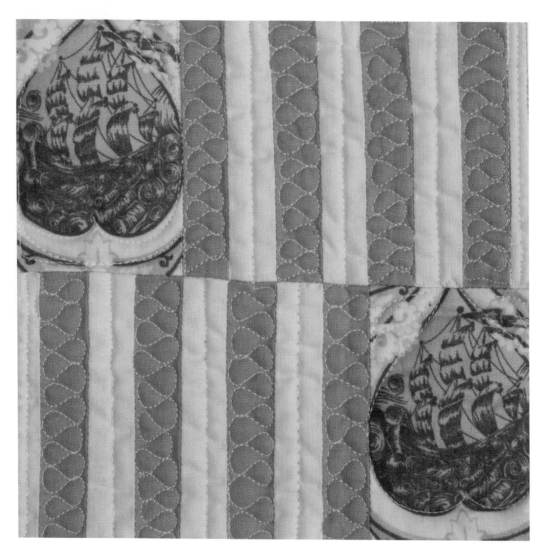

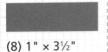 

(8) 1" × 3½"
(2.5cm × 8.9cm)

(8) 1" × 3½"
(2.5cm × 8.9cm)

(2) 2½" × 3½"
(6.4cm × 8.9cm)

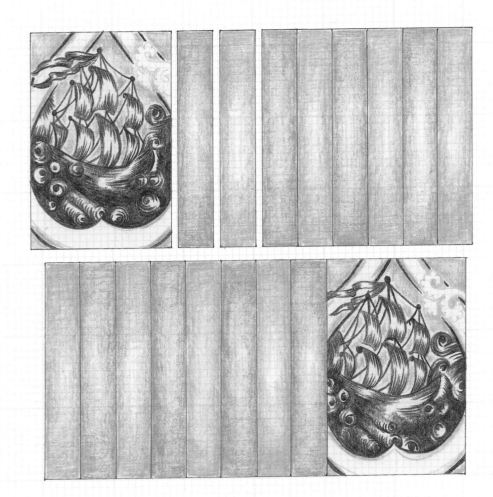

Piecing Diagram

No. of Fabrics: **3** | No. of Pieces: **18**

No. 70

Name: _____

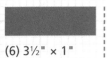 

(6) 3½" × 1"
(8.9cm × 2.5cm)

(6) 3½" × 1"
(8.9cm × 2.5cm)

(3) 6½" × 1½"
(16.5cm × 3.8cm)

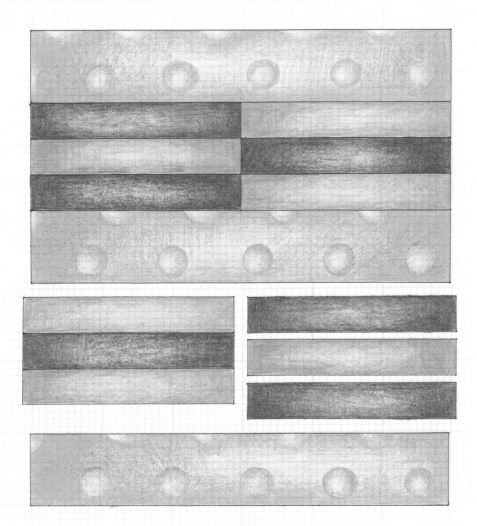

Piecing Diagram

No. of Fabrics: **3** | No. of Pieces: **15**

Blocks 71–85: Squares

The square is the most classic shape in the piecing arsenal. In fact, most blocks throughout history begin with a simple square. Tiny squares can be sewn together to make entirely new patterns, while larger squares can be used to showcase a specific fabric. As simple as a square may be, there is no limit to what we can do with it.

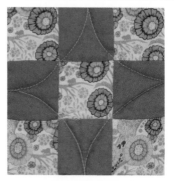

Name: _____

(2) 2½" × 2½"
(6.4cm × 6.4cm)

(4) 1" × 2½"
(2.5cm × 6.4cm)

(4) 3½" × 1"
(8.9cm × 2.5cm)

(2) 2½" × 2½"
(6.4cm × 6.4cm)

(4) 1" × 2½"
(2.5cm × 6.4cm)

(4) 3½" × 1"
(8.9cm × 2.5cm)

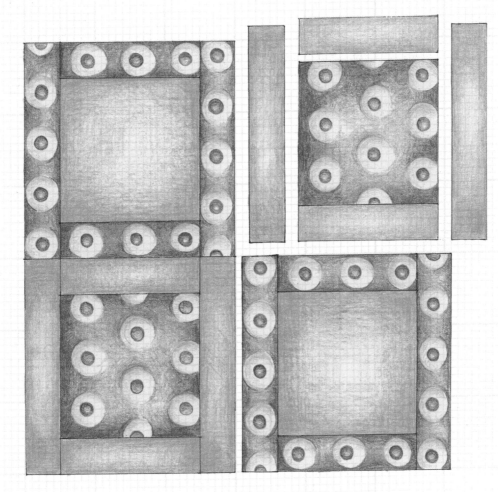

Piecing Diagram

No. of Fabrics: **2** | No. of Pieces: **20**

No. 72

Name: _____

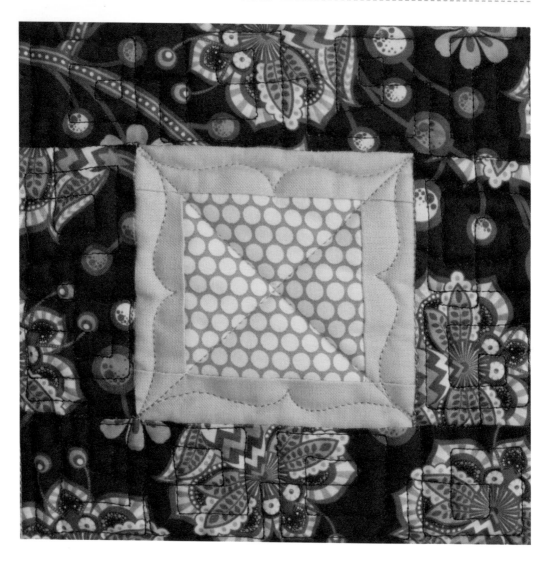

(2) 3½" × 1"
(8.9cm × 2.5cm)

(2) 6½" × 2"
(16.5cm × 5.1cm)

(1) 2½" × 2½"
(6.4cm × 6.4cm)

(2) 1" × 2½"
(2.5cm × 6.4cm)

(2) 2" × 3½"
(5.1cm × 8.9cm)

Piecing Diagram

No. of Fabrics: **3** | No. of Pieces: **9**

163

(2) 1½" × 4½"
(3.8cm × 11.4cm)

(2) 6½" × 1½"
(16.5cm × 3.8cm)

(1) 4½" × 4½"
(11.4cm × 11.4cm)

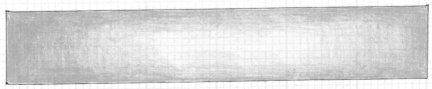

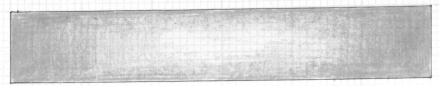

Piecing Diagram

No. of Fabrics: **2** | No. of Pieces: **5**

165

No. 74

(2) 1" × 3"
(2.5cm × 7.6cm)

(1) 1½" × 3½"
(3.8cm × 8.9cm)

(2) 1½" × 4½"
(3.8cm × 11.4cm)

(1) 2½" × 2½"
(6.4cm × 6.4cm)

(2) 4½" × 1"
(11.4cm × 2.5cm)

(1) 1" × 2½"
(2.5cm × 6.4cm)

(2) 6½" × 1½"
(16.5cm × 3.8cm)

(1) 1" × 3½"
(2.5cm × 8.9cm)

Piecing Diagram

No. of Fabrics: **2** | No. of Pieces: **12**

167

(1) 3½" × 3½"
(8.9cm × 8.9cm)

(2) 6½" × 1"
(16.5cm × 2.5cm)

(8) 1½" × 1½"
(3.8cm × 3.8cm)

(8) 1½" × 1½"
(3.8cm × 3.8cm)

(2) 1" × 5½"
(2.5cm × 14cm)

Piecing Diagram

No. of Fabrics: **3** | No. of Pieces: **21**

No. 76

(1) 2½" × 2½"
(6.4cm × 6.4cm)

(1) 5½" × 1½"
(14cm × 3.8cm)

(1) 1½" × 4½"
(3.8cm × 11.4cm)

(1) 1½" × 1½"
(3.8cm × 3.8cm)

(1) 1½" × 6½"
(3.8cm × 16.5cm)

(1) 3½" × 1½"
(8.9cm × 3.8cm)

(1) 1½" × 1½"
(3.8cm × 3.8cm)

(2) 1½" × 2½"
(3.8cm × 6.4cm)

(2) 4½" × 1½"
(11.4cm × 3.8cm)

Piecing Diagram

No. of Fabrics: **3** | No. of Pieces: **11**

171

Name: _____

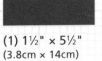
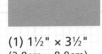

(1) 1½" × 5½"
(3.8cm × 14cm)

(1) 1½" × 4½"
(3.8cm × 11.4cm)

(1) 1½" × 3½"
(3.8cm × 8.9cm)

(1) 3½" × 3½"
(8.9cm × 8.9cm)

(1) 6½" × 1½"
(16.5cm × 3.8cm)

(1) 5½" × 1½"
(14cm × 3.8cm)

(1) 4½" × 1½"
(11.4cm × 3.8cm)

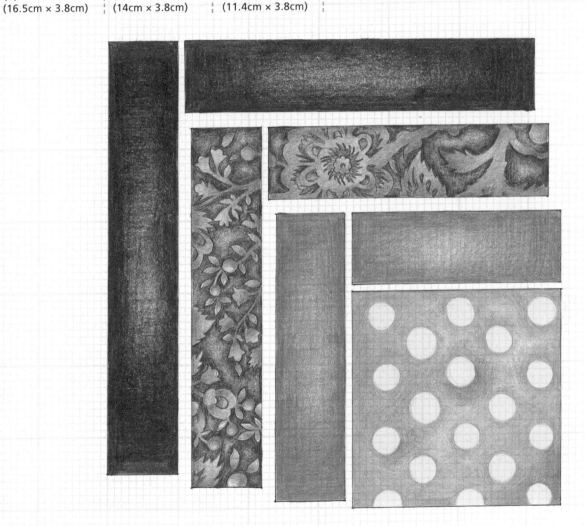

Piecing Diagram

No. of Fabrics: **4** | No. of Pieces: **7**

173

No. 78

Name: _____

(2) 2½" × 1"
(6.4cm × 2.5cm)

(1) 1" × 3½"
(2.5cm × 8.9cm)

(1) 2" × 5"
(6.4cm × 12.7cm)

(1) 1½" × 1½"
(3.8cm × 3.8cm)

(2) 3½" × 1"
(8.9cm × 2.5cm)

(1) 5" × 1½"
(12.7cm × 3.8cm)

(2) 1" × 1½"
(2.5cm × 3.8cm)

(1) 4" × 1"
(10.2cm × 2.5cm)

(1) 6½" × 2"
(16.5cm × 5.1cm)

(2) 1" × 2½"
(2.5cm × 6.4cm)

(1) 1½" × 4"
(3.8cm × 10.2cm)

Piecing Diagram

No. of Fabrics: **2** | No. of Pieces: **15**

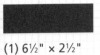   

(1) 6½" × 2½"
(16.5cm × 6.4cm)

(2) 2½" × 2½"
(6.4cm × 6.4cm)

(1) 2½" × 2½"
(6.4cm × 6.4cm)

(1) 6½" × 2½"
(16.5cm × 6.4cm)

Piecing Diagram

No. of Fabrics: **4** | No. of Pieces: **5**

177

No. 80

(4) 1½" × 1½"
(3.8cm × 3.8cm)

(1) 4½" × 2½"
(11.4cm × 6.4cm)

(2) 1½" × 1½"
(3.8cm × 3.8cm)

(1) 2½" × 2½"
(6.4cm × 6.4cm)

(1) 4½" × 4½"
(11.4cm × 11.4cm)

(2) 1½" × 1½"
(3.8cm × 3.8cm)

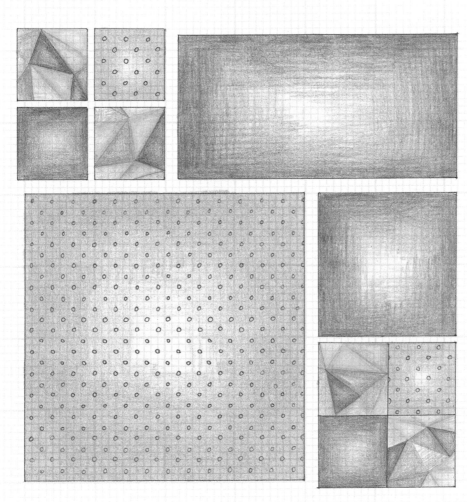

Piecing Diagram

No. of Fabrics: **3** | No. of Pieces: **11**

179

No. 81

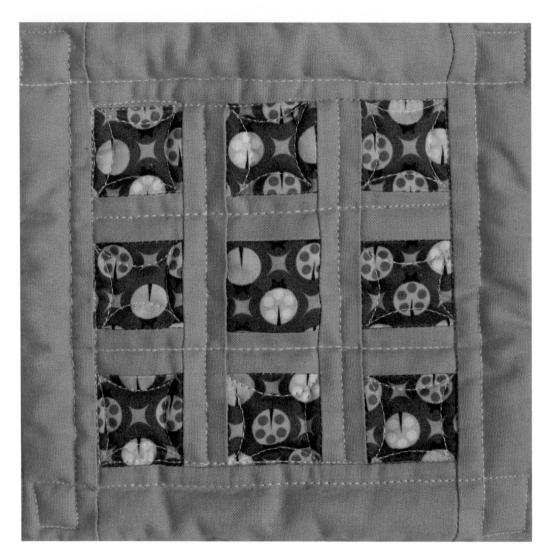

(6) 1½" × 1"
(3.8cm × 2.5cm)

(2) 1" × 4½"
(2.5cm × 11.4cm)

(2) 4½" × 1½"
(11.4cm × 3.8cm)

(2) 6½" × 1½"
(16.5cm × 3.8cm)

(9) 1½" × 1½"
(3.8cm × 3.8cm)

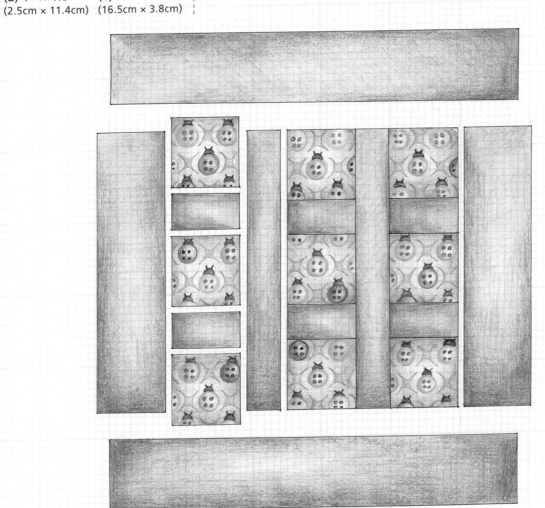

Piecing Diagram

No. of Fabrics: **2** | No. of Pieces: **21**

181

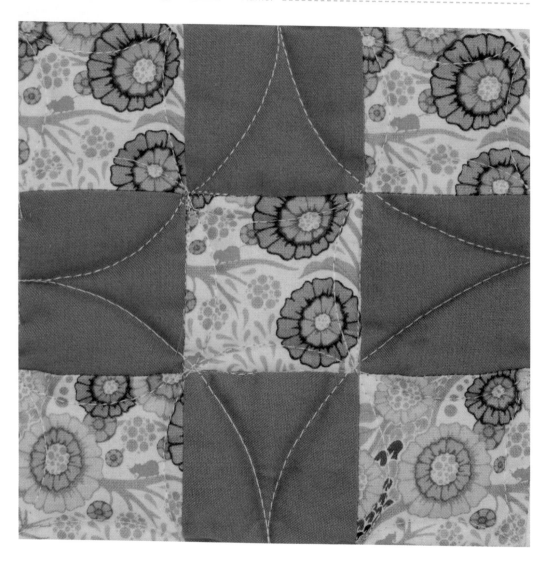

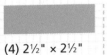 

(4) 2½" × 2½"
(6.4cm × 6.4cm)

(5) 2½" × 2½"
(6.4cm × 6.4cm)

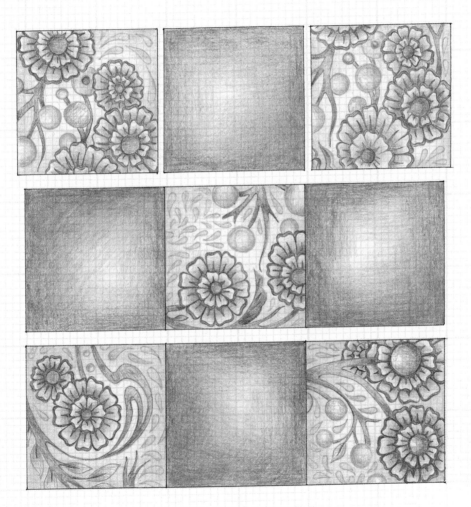

Piecing Diagram

No. of Fabrics: **2** | No. of Pieces: **9**

183

No. 83

(2) 1½" × 4½"
(3.8cm × 11.4cm)

(2) 2½" × 2½"
(6.4cm × 6.4cm)

(2) 2½" × 2½"
(6.4cm × 6.4cm)

(2) 6½" × 1½"
(16.5cm × 3.8cm)

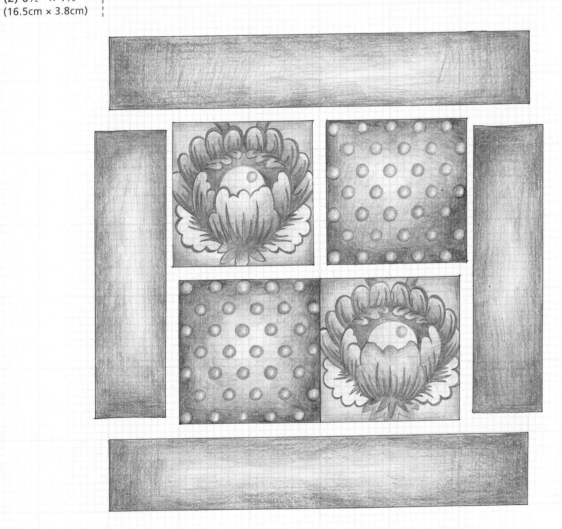

Piecing Diagram

No. of Fabrics: **3** | No. of Pieces: **8**

185

No. 84

(1) 2½" × 2½"
(6.4cm × 6.4cm)

(1) 5½" × 1½"
(14cm × 3.8cm)

(2) 1½" × 2½"
(3.8cm × 6.4cm)

(1) 1½" × 5½"
(3.8cm × 14cm)

(1) 1½" × 4½"
(3.8cm × 11.4cm)

(2) 4½" × 1½"
(11.4cm × 3.8cm)

(1) 1½" × 6½"
(3.8cm × 16.5cm)

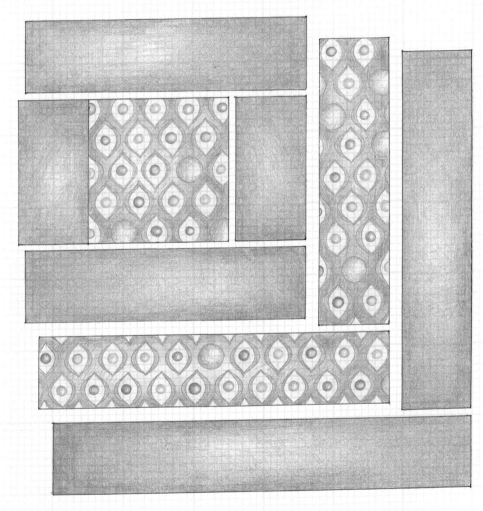

Piecing Diagram

187

(2) 3½" × 3½"
(8.9cm × 8.9cm)

(6) 1½" × 1½"
(3.8cm × 3.8cm)

(8) 1½" × 1½"
(3.8cm × 3.8cm)

(4) 1½" × 1½"
(3.8cm × 3.8cm)

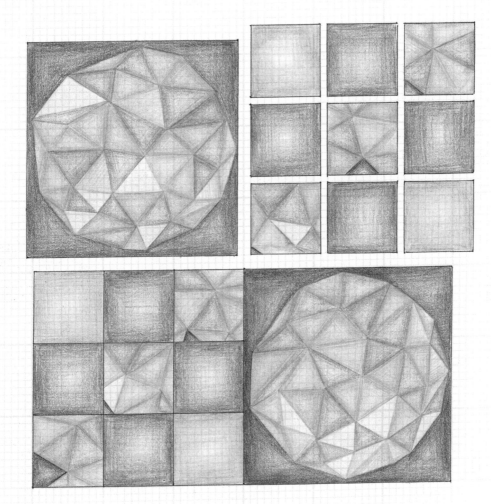

Piecing Diagram

No. of Fabrics: **3** | No. of Pieces: **20**

189

Blocks 86–100: Haiku

The following blocks are more about composition than about the shapes that compose them. I call them haiku blocks because they represent a poetry of shape that feels more organic than in the previous sections. Here you will not find a lot of repetitive shapes or balanced constructions. Instead you will find a composition of pieces that eludes the static nature of more traditional block structures.

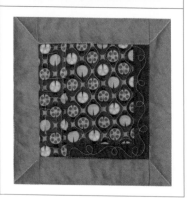

No. 86

Name: _____

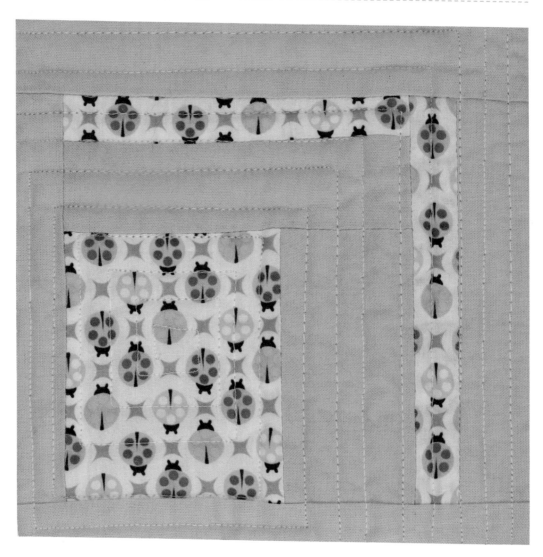

(1) 3" × 3½"
(7.6cm × 8.9cm)

(1) 1" × 5"
(2.5cm × 12.7cm)

(1) 4½" × 1"
(11.4cm × 2.5cm)

(1) 6½" × 1½"
(16.5cm × 3.8cm)

(1) 1" × 5"
(2.5cm × 12.7cm)

(1) 1½" × 5"
(3.8cm × 12.7cm)

(1) 6½" × 1"
(16.5cm × 2.5cm)

(1) 4½" × 1½"
(11.4cm × 2.5cm)

(1) 2" × 3½"
(5.1cm × 8.9cm)

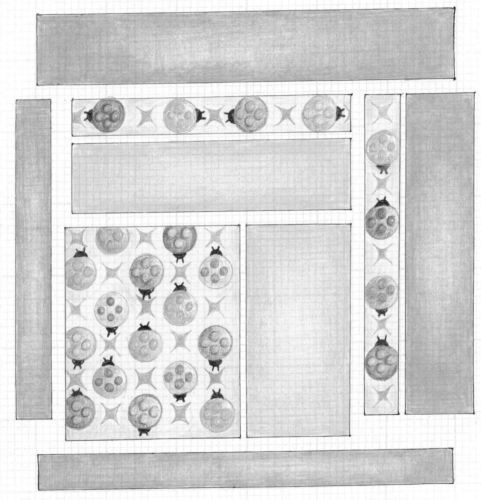

Piecing Diagram

No. of Fabrics: **3** | No. of Pieces: **9**

No. 87

(1) 2½" × 6½"
(6.4cm × 16.5cm)

(1) 1½" × 6½"
(3.8cm × 16.5cm)

(1) 1½" × 2½"
(3.8cm × 6.4cm)

(1) 1½" × 1½"
(3.8cm × 3.8cm)

(1) 3½" × 2½"
(8.9cm × 6.4cm)

(1) 3½" × 1½"
(8.9cm × 3.8cm)

(1) 3½" × 2½"
(8.9cm × 6.4cm)

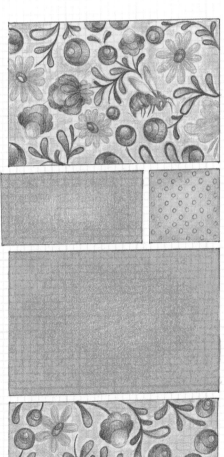

Piecing Diagram

No. of Fabrics: **3** | No. of Pieces: **7**

No. 88

(1) 4½" × 1½"
(11.4cm × 3.8cm)

(1) 3½" × 3½"
(8.9cm × 8.9cm)

(1) 6½" × 2½"
(16.5cm × 6.4cm)

(1) 1½" × 3½"
(3.8cm × 8.9cm)

(2) 1½" × 4½"
(3.8cm × 11.4cm)

Piecing Diagram

No. of Fabrics: **3** | No. of Pieces: **6**

Name: _____

(1) 4" × 5"
(10.2cm × 12.7cm)

(1) 1½" × 2"
(3.8cm × 5.1cm)

(1) 6½" × 1½"
(16.5cm × 3.8cm)

(1) 6½" × 1"
(16.5cm × 2.5cm)

(1) 1" × 5"
(2.5cm × 12.7cm)

(1) 1½" × 5"
(3.8cm × 12.7cm)

(1) 1½" × 3½"
(3.8cm × 8.9cm)

Piecing Diagram

No. of Fabrics: **3** | No. of Pieces: **7**

No. 90

Name: _____

 (1) 2½" × 3½"
(6.4cm × 8.9cm)
(1) 5½" × 2½"
(14cm × 6.4cm)

 (1) 3½" × 3½"
(8.9cm × 8.9cm)

(1) 3½" × 1½"
(8.9cm × 3.8cm)
(1) 1½" × 5½"
(3.8cm × 14cm)

 (1) 3½" × 1½"
(8.9cm × 3.8cm)

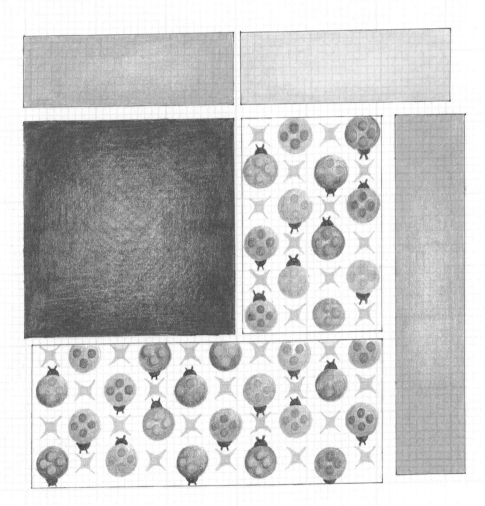

Piecing Diagram

No. of Fabrics: **4** | No. of Pieces: **6**

201

No. 91

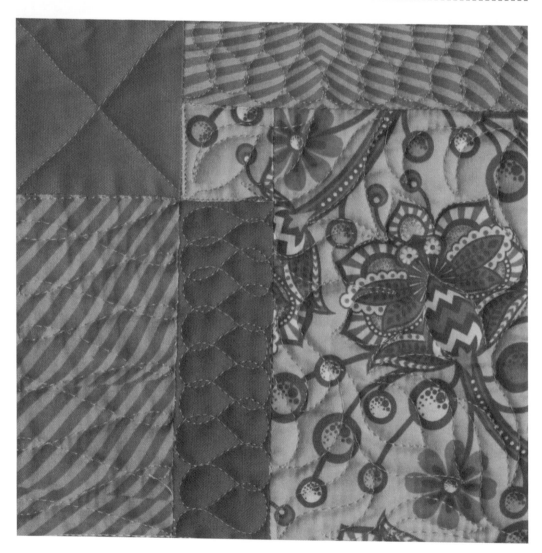

(1) 1½" × 1½"
(3.8cm × 3.8cm)

(1) 3½" × 5½"
(8.9cm × 14cm)

(1) 2½" × 2½"
(6.4cm × 6.4cm)

(1) 1½" × 4½"
(3.8cm × 11.4cm)

(1) 2½" × 4½"
(6.4cm × 11.4cm)

(1) 1½" × 4½"
(3.8cm × 11.4cm)

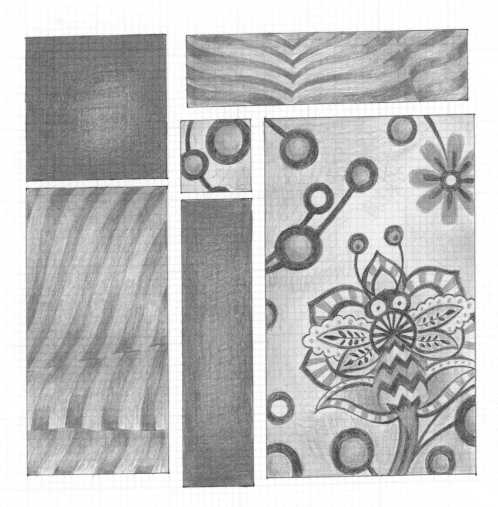

Piecing Diagram

No. of Fabrics: **4** | No. of Pieces: **6**

203

 (1) 4½" × 3½"
(11.4cm × 8.9cm)

 (1) 2½" × 1½"
(6.4cm × 3.8cm)

(1) 1½" × 3½"
(3.8cm × 8.9cm)

(1) 4½" × 2"
(11.4cm × 5.1cm)

(1) 2½" × 1"
(6.4cm × 2.5cm)

 (1) 2½" × 1½"
(6.4cm × 3.8cm)

(1) 1½" × 3½"
(3.8cm × 8.9cm)

(1) 4½" × 2"
(11.4cm × 5.1cm)

(1) 2½" × 1"
(6.4cm × 2.5cm)

Piecing Diagram

No. of Fabrics: **3** | No. of Pieces: **9**

205

(1) 1" × 1½"
(2.5cm × 3.8cm)

(1) 2½" × 2½"
(6.4cm × 6.4cm)

(1) 3" × 1½"
(7.6cm × 3.8cm)

(1) 2½" × 1½"
(6.4cm × 3.8cm)

(1) 3½" × 1½"
(8.9cm × 3.8cm)

(1) 4½" × 1½"
(11.4cm × 3.8cm)

(2) 4½" × 1½"
(11.4cm × 3.8cm)

(2) 1½" × 6½"
(3.8cm × 16.5cm)

Piecing Diagram

No. of Fabrics: **3** | No. of Pieces: **10**

207

No. 94

Name: _____

(1) 2½" × 2"
(6.4cm × 5.1cm)

(1) 3½" × 1"
(8.9cm × 2.5cm)

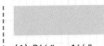

(1) 1½" × 5½"
(3.8cm × 14cm)

(1) 3½" × 1½"
(8.9cm × 3.8cm)

(1) 6½" × 1½"
(16.5cm × 3.8cm)

(1) 5½" × 4"
(14cm × 10.2cm)

Piecing Diagram

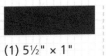

(1) 5½" × 1"
(14cm × 2.5cm)

(1) 4½" × 4"
(11.4cm × 10.2cm)

(1) 5½" × 2½"
(14cm × 6.4cm)

(1) 1½" × 4"
(3.8cm × 10.2cm)

(1) 1½" × 6½"
(3.8cm × 16.5cm)

Piecing Diagram

No. of Fabrics: **3** | No. of Pieces: **5**

211

Name: _____

(1) 1½" × 6½"
(3.8cm × 16.5cm)

(3) 1½" × 3½"
(3.8cm × 8.9cm)

(1) 3½" × 1½"
(8.9cm × 3.8cm)

(1) 3½" × 3½"
(8.9cm × 8.9cm)

(1) 1½" × 5½"
(3.8cm × 14cm)

(2) 1½" × 2½"
(3.8cm × 6.4cm)

Piecing Diagram

No. of Fabrics: **3** | No. of Pieces: **9**

No. 97

Name: _____

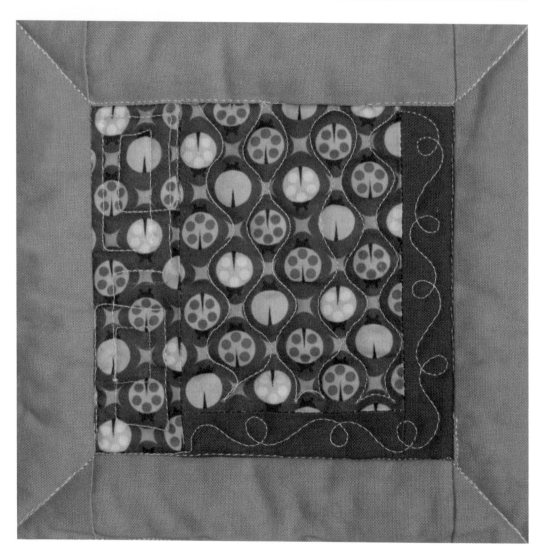

(1) 3" × 4"
(7.6cm × 10.2cm)

(1) 3" × 1"
(7.6cm × 2.5cm)

(2) 4½" × 1½"
(11.4cm × 3.8cm)

(1) 1½" × 4½"
(3.8cm × 11.4cm)

(1) 1" × 4½"
(2.5cm × 11.4cm)

(2) 1½" × 6½"
(3.8cm × 16.5cm)

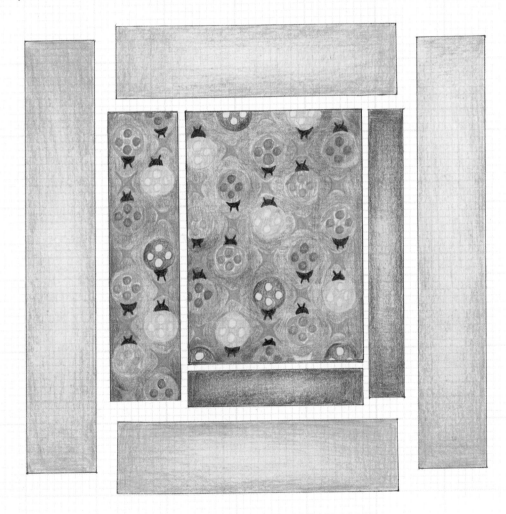

Piecing Diagram

No. of Fabrics: **3** | No. of Pieces: **8**

(1) 1½" × 5½"
(3.8cm × 14cm)

(1) 2½" × 1½"
(6.4cm × 3.8cm)

(1) 3½" × 2½"
(8.9cm × 6.4cm)

(1) 3½" × 4½"
(8.9cm × 11.4cm)

(1) 1½" × 1½"
(3.8cm × 3.8cm)

(1) 2½" × 5½"
(6.4cm × 14cm)

Piecing Diagram

No. of Fabrics: **3** | No. of Pieces: **6**

No. 99

Name: _____

(1) 6½" × 1½"
(16.5cm × 3.8cm)

(1) 1½" × 3½"
(3.8cm × 8.9cm)

(1) 1½" × 3½"
(3.8cm × 8.9cm)

(1) 2½" × 2½"
(6.4cm × 6.4cm)

(1) 1½" × 2½"
(3.8cm × 6.4cm)

(1) 3½" × 2½"
(8.9cm × 6.4cm)

(1) 4½" × 3½"
(11.4cm × 8.9cm)

Piecing Diagram

No. of Fabrics: **3** | No. of Pieces: **7**

Name: _____

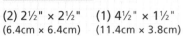  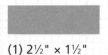

(2) 2½" × 2½"
(6.4cm × 6.4cm)

(1) 4½" × 1½"
(11.4cm × 3.8cm)

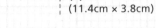

(1) 4½" × 4½"
(11.4cm × 11.4cm)

(1) 2½" × 1½"
(6.4cm × 3.8cm)

(1) 2½" × 1½"
(6.4cm × 3.8cm)

(1) 4½" × 1½"
(11.4cm × 3.8cm)

Piecing Diagram

No. of Fabrics: **3** | No. of Pieces: **7**

221

CHAPTER TWO

THE QUILTS

There are many ways to tackle the finishing of your quilt, and I have provided you with five possible solutions in various sizes, and with minimal complexity. Each possibility will require a different number of blocks and setting fabrics, and each is designed to let your blocks shine.

Three Methods for Choosing Colors

Near sighted
the limited palette

Choosing a limited palette means that you're working with only a few colors. Don't let the name fool you—there is a lot of room to move around within a limited palette.

In *Trellis* (page 228), I chose to work with only blues, greens and yellows. Within that palette of three colors, I had the option of pulling in hundreds of shades of those colors. Because all three are next to each other on the color wheel, I knew they would blend seamlessly into one another. This gave me a lot of options. From blue I could pull in everything from navy to a soft sky blue; add green, and I can pull in all the colors that fall between blue and green, like aqua and teal. I added a third color, yellow, to bring a little sunshine to the color scheme. Yellow sits next to green on the color wheel and allowed me to add some lime and more yellow-hued greens.

Tunnel vision
the monochromatic palette

Mono, meaning single, and chroma, meaning color, put together simply mean a single color. The monochromatic palette is all about your lights and your darks.

In *Skyline* (page 234), I focused on gray as the single color of the quilt. Gray at its darkest is black and at its lightest is white. This scale of dark to light is called the value or the shade of a color. Having every shade between white and black also gave me a lot to work with when making my blocks. Add in the option of prints, dots, stripes and solids, and that pool of options gets even deeper.

When making a monochromatic quilt, value is king! The success of each block comes down to putting enough contrast into each piece. If I put two white fabrics next to each other, you won't see the block. But if I put a black and white next to each other, that might be too much. There must be a balance so that you can see the shapes in each block without creating an optical illusion that might make you dizzy!

Scrap happy
the anything goes palette

The Scrap Happy palette is for the person who throws all the chips in the air just to see where they fall.

I approached *Gridlock* (page 240) this way. I looked at each block and made them one by one without looking at the block I made before or looking ahead to the blocks I was going to make. I knew I wanted my finished quilt to blend from one color to the next, and for that to happen I needed every variation of every color. For each block I began with a main fabric that was going to be the star of the block and then added in little pieces that complemented it. This method of fabric selection will make the whole worth more than the sum of its parts. Each individual block was nice, but when all of the blocks were put together, it made a spectacular rainbow of fabrics and pieces.

Tools

Must Have Tools

- Rotary cutter
- Cutting mat
- Ruler
- Marking tools (such as chalk pencils, disappearing ink pens, etc.)
- Scissors
- Thread
- Sewing machine (although you can hand sew, but it will take forever)
- Iron
- Ironing board
- Seam ripper

Handy but Optional Tools

- 6½" × 6½" (16.5cm ×16.5cm) ruler for squaring up your blocks
- ¼" (6mm) machine foot with guide (this will make your seams more accurate)
- Spray starch alternative (great for making crisp seams and taking the stretch out of fabrics)

Sewing Machine

Ruler

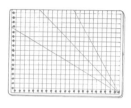

Cutting Mat

Rotary Cutter

Thread

Spray Starch Alternative

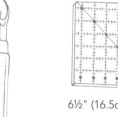

6½" (16.5cm) ruler

Seam Ripper

Iron

Scissors

Ironing Board

¼" (6mm) Piecing Foot

Chalk Pencil

Tips

Create a Design Wall

A design wall is a great thing to have for laying out your blocks and deciding how to arrange them. Making a design wall is easy. Fabric will adhere to a number of fibrous surfaces like felt or fleece. The easiest way to make a temporary or permanent design wall is to tack a sheet of batting to a clear space on the wall. Batting comes in larger sizes, so you don't have to piece together lengths off the bolt like you do with fleece or felt. Your cotton fabric pieces will "stick" to the wall but are easily removed, allowing you to move blocks around until you find the best arrangement.

Separate and Meditate!

Separate and label all of your pieces, and set aside everything but the pieces you are using. This will help keep everything organized and cut down on errors while sewing. Think of this as a meditation. Setting your blocks together is a repetitive activity. Put on some music and zone out to the gentle hum of your sewing machine. If you happen to thrive on chaos, then still keep your pieces organized but turn up the volume.

Make Accurate Seams

Generally you will press your seams to one side. However, follow the path of least resistance when pressing. If you have a lot of seams on one side and none on the other side of your seam, then press to the side without any seams. If you have a lot of seams on both sides, then press that seam open.

Be sure to use accurate ¼" (6mm) seams in all constructions!

What to Do With Your Triangle Scraps

When using this method of creating triangles, you will end up with a scrap set of small triangles for every triangle you create. The excess triangle pieces that get trimmed away have two very important characteristics: They are already paired and right sides together, and they are already trimmed and exactly the same size as each other. Instead of throwing these seemingly useless, yet completely adorable little triangle pairs in the trash, re-purpose them! Get in the habit of sewing them together on the longer bias edge and set them aside. When all the blocks from the triangle chapter are complete, get them back out and press them, seams open. There are an infinite number of ways to arrange this little triangle scrap block. You can use them as a coordinating throw pillow for your final quilt or just piece them into your backing for a two-sided quilt!

Trellis

The *Trellis* quilt is a throw-sized quilt that makes a perfect rainy-day-lounge-on-the-couch-curled-up-with-a-good-book quilt. The design of *Trellis* frames and highlights each block as a small jewel to be admired while creating a larger pattern on its own.

THROW

Finished Size: 73" × 73"
(185.4cm × 185.4cm)
Number of Blocks: 64

Fabric

(Based on 44"/45"
[111.8cm/114.3cm] fabrics)
Block Frame: 2½ yds. (2.3m)
Sashing: 1¾ yds. (1.6m)
Binding: ⅝ yds. (.6m)
(cut 8 strips)
Backing: 4½ yds. (4.1m)

Cutting Guide

**From Block Frame
Fabric Cut:**
(128) 1½" × 6½"
(3.8cm × 16.5cm)
(128) 1½" × 8½"
(3.8cm × 21.6cm)
(144) 1½" × 1½"
(3.8cm × 3.8cm)
**From Sashing
Fabric cut:**
(144) 4" × 1½"
(10.2cm × 3.8cm)
(63) 8½" × 1½"
(21.6cm × 3.8cm)
(18) 5" × 1½"
(12.7cm × 3.8cm)

A Tip on Lining Up Your Block Rows and Sashing Strips

Find the center of each framed block and mark it with a straight pin. You can find the center by folding the block in half and matching the seams. Use your finger to make a small crease where the center is. Line up the center of each frame square on your sashing strip with the center of each frame block and use the pin that marks the center of your frame block to pin those points together. Pin each end of your block row and sashing strip, lining up the raw edges. I know this seems like a lot of pinning, but it will ensure that your quilt top is square, lays flat and that all the pieces line up in the end.

Cutting Diagrams

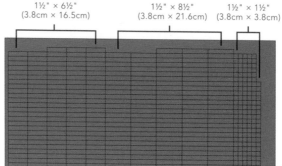

1½" × 6½"
(3.8cm × 16.5cm)   1½" × 8½"
(3.8cm × 21.6cm)   1½" × 1½"
(3.8cm × 3.8cm)

Selvedge Edge   Block Frame Fabric

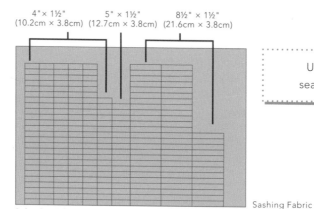

4" × 1½"
(10.2cm × 3.8cm)   5" × 1½"
(12.7cm × 3.8cm)   8½" × 1½"
(21.6cm × 3.8cm)

Selvedge Edge   Sashing Fabric

Use accurate ¼" (6mm)
seams in all constructions.

Framing your blocks

1. Sew one 1½" × 6½" (3.8cm × 16.5cm) frame piece to the right side of your block, right sides together (RST), making sure to line up your edges. Press toward the frame piece.

2. Sew another 1½" × 6½" (3.8cm × 16.5cm) frame piece to the left side of your block, RST, making sure to line up your edges. Press toward the frame piece.

3. Sew one 1½" × 8½" (3.8cm × 21.6cm) frame piece to the top of the unit competed in step 2, RST, making sure to line up your edges. Press towards the frame piece.

4. Sew one 1½" × 8½" (3.8cm × 21.6cm) frame piece to the bottom of the unit completed in step 3, RST, making sure to line up your edges. Press towards the frame piece.

5. Repeat steps 1 through 4 to frame all 64 blocks for your quilt.

Connecting the Blocks and Building Your Rows

6. Sew one 4" × 1½" (10.2cm × 3.8cm) sashing piece to one 1½" × 1½" (3.8cm × 3.8cm) frame piece, RST, along the short edges. Press toward the framed block.

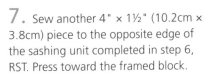

7. Sew another 4" × 1½" (10.2cm × 3.8cm) piece to the opposite edge of the sashing unit completed in step 6, RST. Press toward the framed block.

8. Repeat steps 6 and 7 to make a total of 72 vertical sashing units.

9. Using nine vertical sashing strips and eight framed blocks, build your row by alternating these units beginning and ending with a vertical sashing strip.

10. Repeat steps 6 through 9 to make a total of eight rows.

Building the Horizontal Sashing Stripes

11. Sew one 5" × 1½" (12.7cm × 3.8cm) sashing piece to one 1½" × 1½" (3.8cm × 3.8cm) frame piece.

12. Using seven 8½" × 1½" (21.6cm × 3.8cm) sashing pieces and seven 1½" × 1½" (3.8cm × 3.8cm) frame pieces, sew your sashing, RST, by alternating the two pieces beginning with a sashing piece and ending with a frame piece. Press all seams toward the frame pieces.

13. Sew the unit made in step 11 to the beginning of the unit in step 12, RST. Press seams toward the frame piece.

14. Sew one 5" × 1½" (12.7cm × 3.8cm) sashing piece to the end of the unit made in step 13, RST.

15. Repeat steps 11 through 14 to make a total of nine horizontal sashing strips.

Assemble the Quilt Top

16. To complete your quilt top, sew your horizontal sashing strips and your block rows, right sides together, according to the assembly diagram. (See page 230 for a tip on lining up block rows and sashing strips.)

Assembly diagram

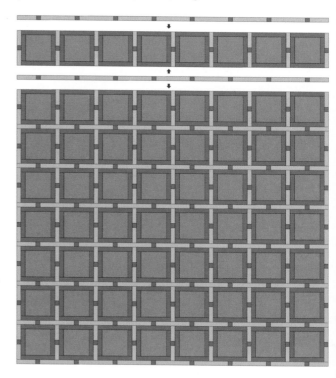

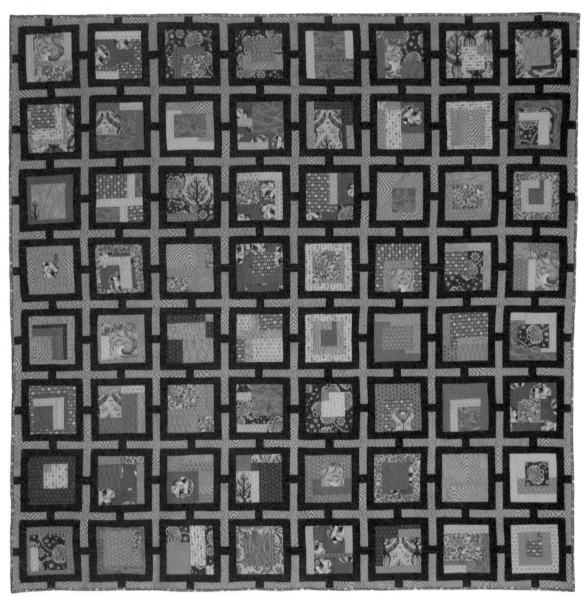

Quilted by Angela Walters

Skyline

kyline is a twin-sized option that mimics a city skyline. When I am walking through city streets at night, I love it when people leave the lights on in their apartments, and you get a small glimpse into the way other people live. Think of each block as a peek behind the curtain.

TWIN

Finished Size: 66" × 89"
  (167.6cm × 226.1cm)
Number of Blocks: 70

Fabric

(Based on 44"/45"
  [111.8cm/114.3cm] fabrics)
Sashing: 3¼ yds. (3m)
Binding: ⅝ yds. (.6cm)
  (cut 8 strips)
Backing: 5½ yds. (5m)

Cutting Guide

From Sashing Fabric cut:
A - (2) 87½" × 2½" (222.3cm × 6.4cm)
  (side borders)
B - (1) 66½" × 2½" (168.9cm × 6.4cm)
  (bottom border)
C - (8) 87½" × 1½" (222.3cm × 3.8cm)
  (vertical sashing strips)
D - (1) 46½" × 6½" (118.1cm × 16.5cm)
E - (1) 25½" × 6½" (64.8cm × 16.5cm)
F - (1) 39½" × 6½" (100.3cm × 16.5cm)
G - (1) 4½" × 6½" (105.4cm × 16.5cm)
H - (1) 32½" × 6½" (54.6cm × 16.5cm)
I - (1) 46½" × 6½" (118.1cm × 16.5cm)
J - (1)11½" × 6½" (29.2cm × 16.5cm)
K - (1) 60½" × 6½" (153.7cm × 16.5cm)
L - (1) 39½" × 6½" (100.3cm × 16.5cm)
M - (61) 6½" × 1½" (16.5cm × 3.8cm)

Sashing and Strips

In this layout option, every column of blocks is assembled differently, which means that almost every piece is cut at a different length. Cut your sashing and column strips, lengthwise, from the fabric so that you don't have to piece them together. This will allow your quilt top to come together more smoothly and eliminate those pesky extra seams.

As you cut your strips, assign a letter that corresponds to that strip. Mark your strips by writing the letter on a scrap of paper and pinning it to that strip.

Pin! Pin! Pin!

When sewing long, skinny strips, use a lot of pins! Begin by finding the center of the strip and line that center up with the center of your column. Pin. Then pin each end of the strip to the end of the column. It's likely that the columns and sashing strips will be slightly different lengths. Distribute any extra length evenly through the sashing strip and pin every 3 or 4 inches (7.6cm–10.2cm). This is good practice any time you are sewing long seams such as borders. Pin! Pin! Pin! It's worth the extra effort.

Use accurate ¼" (6mm)
seams in all constructions.

Assemble the Quilt Top

Since *Skyline* is not based on a traditional block structure, we're going to put this one together a little differently.

Each column has a recipe that consists of sashing strips (**M**), 6½" (16.5cm) blocks and a corresponding 6½" (16.5cm) strip based on the letters that you assigned to each piece when you were cutting (e.g. **D**, **E**, **F**, etc). The column letter and the 6½" (16.5cm) strip letter are the same.

Always press toward the sashing fabric.

Sew the bottom strip (**B**) on last, after all of your columns are completed and sewn together.

Use the **Column Recipes** to assemble the columns, always sewing right sides together and pressing toward the sashing.

Column Recipes

D: 6 blocks, 5 sashing strips (**M**)
E: 9 blocks, 8 sashing strips (**M**)
F: 7 blocks, 6 sashing strips (**M**)
G: 12 blocks, 11 sashing strips (**M**)
H: 8 blocks, 7 sashing strips (**M**)
I: 6 blocks, 5 sashing strips (**M**)
J: 11 blocks, 10 sashing strips (**M**)
K: 4 blocks, 3 sashing strips (**M**)
L: 7 blocks, 6 sashing strips (**M**)

Use the **Assembly Diagram** (page 238) to complete your quilt top. Sew the bottom strip (**B**) on last after all the columns are completed.

Cutting Diagram

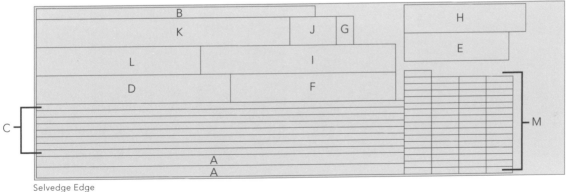

Selvedge Edge

Assembly Diagram

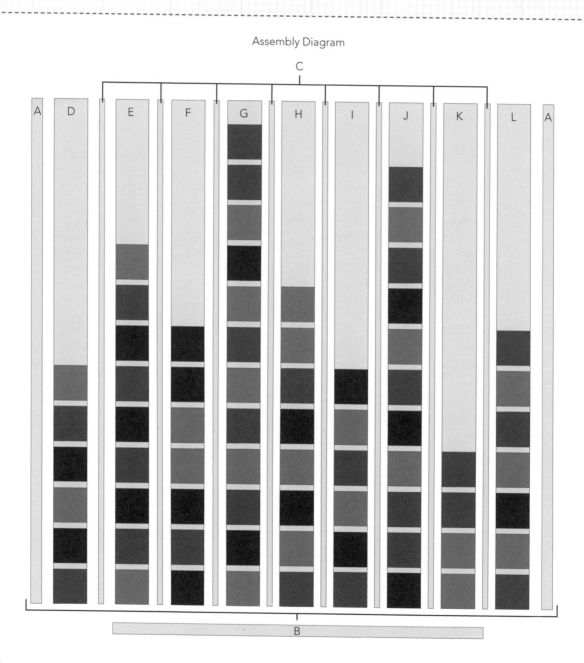

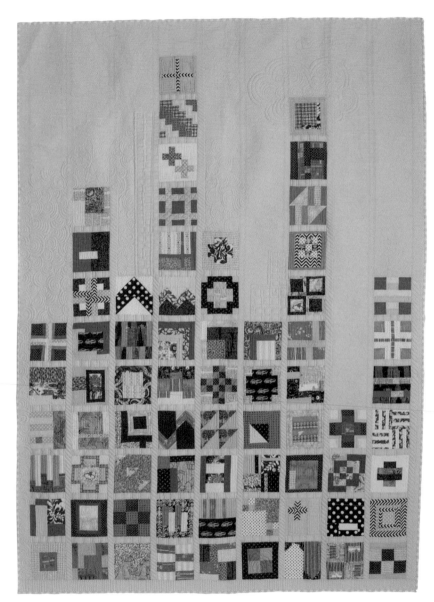

Quilted by Angela Walters

Gridlock

The *Gridlock* quilt is, perhaps, the simplest of all the quilt layouts. One hundred blocks are evenly spaced and set within this queen-sized option. This quilt is about the blocks and nothing else. The background simply falls away, allowing each block to shine on its own.

QUEEN

Finished Size: 90" × 90"
   (228.6cm × 228.6cm)
Number of Blocks: 100

Fabric
(Based on 44"/45"
   [111.8cm/114.3cm] fabrics)
Sashing & Borders: 4½ yds. (4.1m)
Binding: ⅝ yds. (.6m)
   (cut 9 strips)
Backing: 8¼ yds. (7.5m)

Cutting Guide
**From Sashing & Border
Fabric cut:**
(18) 2½" (6.4cm) × Width of Fabric
   (WOF)
(2) 90½" × 6½" (229.9cm × 16.5cm)
(2) 78½" × 6½" (199.4cm × 16.5cm)
(90) 6½" × 2½" (16.5cm × 6.4cm)

Sewing

1. Sew two 2½" (6.4cm) × WOF strips with right sides together, along the short ends, to create nine long 78½" × 2½" (199.4cm × 6.4cm) sashing strips.

> Use accurate ¼" (6mm) seams in all constructions.

2. Sew one 6½" × 2½" (16.5cm × 6.4cm) sashing piece to the right side of one 6½" × 6½" (16.5cm × 16.5cm) pieced block. Press towards the sashing fabric.

3. Repeat step 2 until your row consists of ten 6½" × 6½" (16.5cm × 16.5cm) pieced blocks and nine 6½" × 2½" (16.5cm × 6.4cm) sashing pieces, beginning with a pieced block and ending with a pieced block. Press all seams toward the sashing fabric.

Cutting Diagram

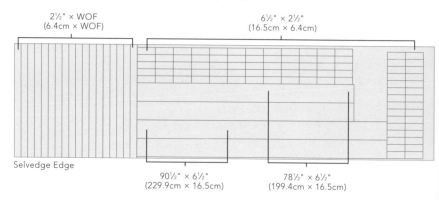

2½" × WOF
(6.4cm × WOF)

6½" × 2½"
(16.5cm × 6.4cm)

Selvedge Edge

90½" × 6½"
(229.9cm × 16.5cm)

78½" × 6½"
(199.4cm × 16.5cm)

4. Repeat steps 1–3 to create a total of ten rows.

5. With RST, sew one 78½" x 2½" (199.4cm × 6.4cm) sashing strip to the bottom edge of a block row. Press toward the sashing fabric.

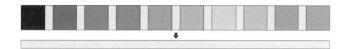

6. Repeat step 5, adding a sashing strip to a block row to create a total of 9 units.

Assemble the Quilt Top

7. With RST, sew all 9 blocks/sashing rows together Sew block row 10 to block/sashing row 9 last. Make sure to line up your blocks so that the vertical columns line up as well as the horizontal rows. Use a lot of pins! (See Assembly Diagram on page 244.)

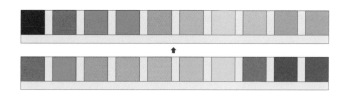

8. Sew a 78½" × 6½" (199.4cm × 16.5cm) border strip to the left edge of quilt, RST. Press toward the border fabric.

9. Sew a 78½" × 6½" (199.4cm × 16.5cm) border strip to the right edge of your quilt, RST. Press toward the border fabric.

10. Add the top and bottom borders last. Press toward the border fabric.

*Your quilt top center should consist of 10 block rows and 9 sashing strips, beginning and ending with a block row.

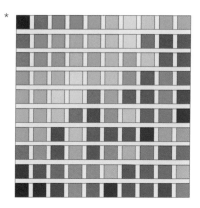

243

Assembly Diagram

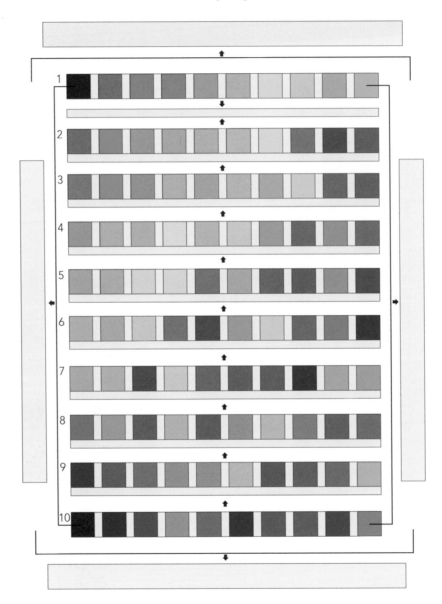

Quilted by Angela Walters

City Planner

KING

Finished Size: 104" × 104"
   (264.2cm × 264.2cm)
Number of Blocks: 100

Fabric

(Based on 44"/45"
   [111.8cm/114.3cm] fabrics)
Sashing no.1: 3⅝ yds. (3.3m)
Sashing no.2: 3½ yds. (3.2m)
Binding: ⅞ yds. (.8m)
   (cut 9 strips)
Backing: 9⅜ yds. (8.6m)

Cutting Guide
From Sashing no.1
Fabric cut:
(6) 104½" × 4½" (265.4cm × 11.4cm)
(110) 4½" × 3½ 1(11.4cm × 8.9cm)

From Sashing no.2
Fabric cut:
(5) 104½" × 4½" (265.4cm × 11.4cm)
(110) 4½" × 3½" (11.4cm × 8.9cm)

The *City Planner* quilt brings to mind an aerial view of the perfect neighborhood, with wide, clean streets and well-manicured yards. This one-hundred-block option serves as an organized little community of blocks all in a row. The two-toned setting fabrics will create a stripe effect that will allow your blocks to nestle comfortably into place.

Use accurate ¼" (6mm) seams in all constructions.

Sewing

1. Sew one 4½" × 3½" (11.4cm × 8.9cm) (sashing no. 1) to one 4½" × 3½" (11.4cm × 8.9cm) (sashing no. 2), RST, along the 4½" (11.4cm) edge. Press your seams open. (Pressing the seams open here will cut down seam bulk when they are sewn to your pieced blocks.)

2. Repeat step 1 to make a total of 110 units. This is your block sashing.

3. Sew one sashing unit to the left side of one pieced block, RST. Press toward the sashing unit.

4. Repeat step 3, sewing a total of ten block/sashing units

Cutting Diagrams

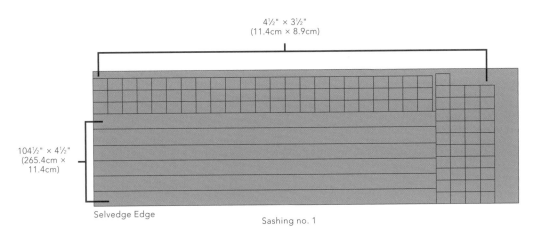

4½" × 3½"
(11.4cm × 8.9cm)

104½" × 4½"
(265.4cm ×
11.4cm)

Selvedge Edge

Sashing no. 1

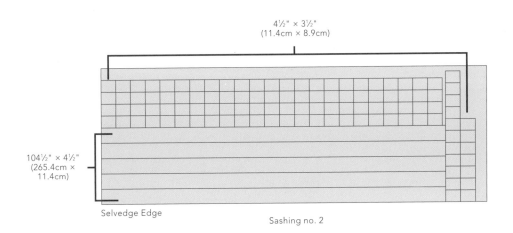

4½" × 3½"
(11.4cm × 8.9cm)

104½" × 4½"
(265.4cm ×
11.4cm)

Selvedge Edge

Sashing no. 2

5. Sew all ten block/sashing units together, RST, adding one final sashing unit (as sewn in step 1) to the end of your row. Press all seams toward the sashing units.

6. Repeat steps 3 through 5, this time making sure that sashing fabric no. 2 is reversed and at the top of each sashing unit.

7. Sew one 104½" × 4½" (265.4cm × 11.4cm) sashing fabric no. 2 strip to the bottom edge of row one, RST. Press toward the sashing strip.

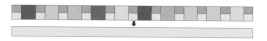

8. Sew the unit completed in step 7, RST, to one pieced block/sashing unit completed in step 6. Press toward the sashing strip. (This is your completed row 1.)

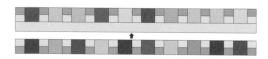

9. Repeat steps 1 through 8 to make a total of five completed rows.

Assemble the Quilt Top

10. With RST, sew one 104½" × 4½" (265.4cm × 11.4cm) sashing no. 1 piece to row 1.

11. Repeat step 10 with rows 2 though 5.

12. Add the remaining 104½" × 4½" (265.4cm × 11.4cm) sashing no. 1 piece to the lower edge of row 5.

Assembly Diagram

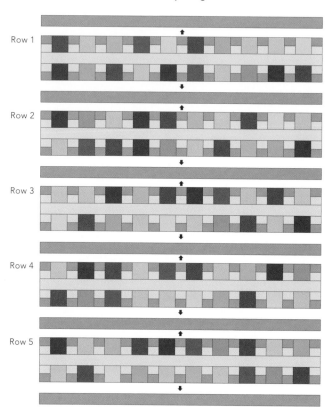

Sliding Scale

FULL/QUEEN

Finished Size: 80" × 93"
(203.2cm × 236.2cm)
Number of Blocks: 70

Fabric

*(Based on 44"/45"
[111.8cm/114.3cm] fabrics)*
Sashing: 4½ yds. (4.1m)
Binding: ⅝ yds. (.6m)
(cut 9 strips)
Backing: 8½ yds. (7.8m)

Cutting Guide

From Sashing Fabric cut:
(11) 80½" × 3½"
(204.5cm × 8.9cm)
(10) 18½" × 6½"
(47cm × 16.5cm)
(10) 8½" × 6½"
(21.6cm × 16.5cm)
(60) 6½" × 2½"
(16.5cm × 6.4cm)

*S*liding Scale is another queen-sized option that highlights your blocks while setting them slightly off balance. If perfection isn't your thing, and lining everything up perfectly sounds a little boring to you, then this might be your best fit.

Building Your Rows

1. Sew seven 6½" × 6½" (16.5cm × 16.5cm) pieced blocks and six 6½" × 2½" (16.5cm × 6.4cm) sashing pieces, RST, beginning with a pieced block and ending with a pieced block. Press toward the sashing fabric.

2. Repeat step 1 to make a total of ten rows.

Use accurate ¼" (6mm) seams in all constructions.

Cutting Diagram

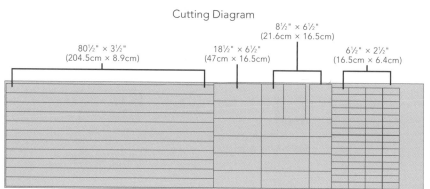

80½" × 3½"
(204.5cm × 8.9cm)

18½" × 6½"
(47cm × 16.5cm)

8½" × 6½"
(21.6cm × 16.5cm)

6½" × 2½"
(16.5cm × 6.4cm)

Selvedge Edge

3. Sew one 6½" × 18½" (16.5cm × 47cm) piece, RST, to the beginning of rows 1, 3, 5, 7 and 9. Press toward the sashing fabric.

4. Sew one 6½" × 8½" (16.5cm × 21.6cm) piece, RST, to the end of rows 1, 3, 5, 7 and 9. Press toward the sashing fabric.

5. Sew one 6½" × 8½" (16.5cm × 21.6cm) piece, RST, to the beginning of rows 2, 4, 6, 8 and 10. Press toward the sashing fabric.

6. Sew one 6½" × 18½" (16.5cm × 47cm) piece to the end of rows 2, 4, 6, 8 and 10. Press toward the sashing fabric.

Assemble the Quilt Top

7. Assemble your quilt according to the assembly diagram alternating sashing strips and block rows. Begin and end with a sashing strip. Always press toward the sashing fabric.

Assembly Diagram

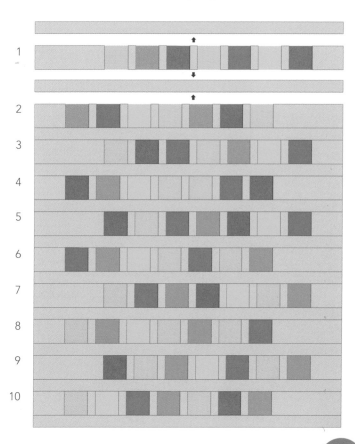

251

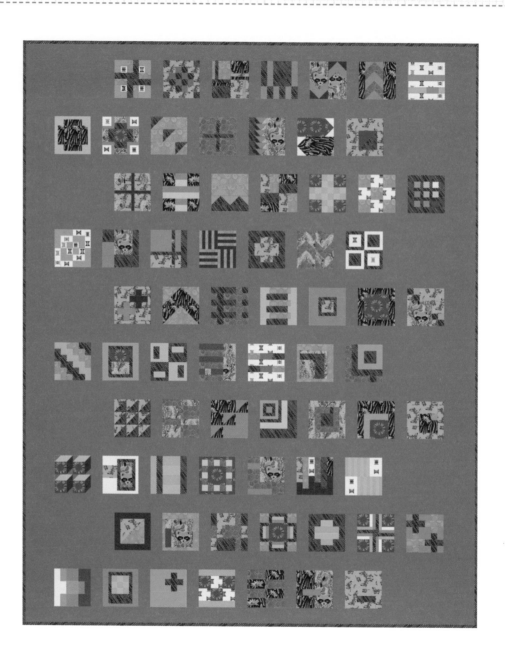

Tips for Finishing Your Quilt

Preparing Your Backing and Batting

No matter which method of quilting you choose, your batting and backing should measure at least six to eight inches (15.2cm to 20.3cm) larger than your quilt top.

Every method of quilting besides long-arm machine quilting will require you to baste your quilt top, batting and backing before you begin quilting. Basting is achieved with long stitches or curved safety pins to hold all three layers together, and to eliminate the shifting of these layers during the actual quilting process.

Choosing a Quilting Method

Choosing a method of quilting is as important as the quilt top itself. There are many factors that go into making this decision, the two biggest of which are time and money. Sending your quilt top to a long-arm quilter can be expensive, but it can also yield gorgeous results when sent to someone with real talent. Hand quilting won't cost you a lot of money, but it can

take months, or sometimes years, to complete. It is important to evaluate the quilt top and decide which method would best compliment it. The quilting should enhance the piecing.

Binding Your Finished Quilt

1. Cut the binding strips 2¼" (5.7cm) wide. Join all the strips with diagonal seams. Cut off excess seam allowances and press the seams open.

2. Press one end under in a 45° angle.

3. Fold and press the binding strips in half lengthwise with wrong sides together, starting with the folded corner.

4. Place the binding along one edge of the project with raw edges together. Using a ¼" (6mm) seam, start sewing along the edge, leaving several inches of tail at the beginning. Stop sewing ¼" (6mm) away from the corner and backstitch.

5. Fold the binding away at a 90° angle.

6. Fold the binding back along the second straight edge.

7. Continue sewing along the second edge, starting ¼" (6mm) away from the corner and backstitching at the beginning.

8. Continue in this way around the entire project. Cut the end of the binding strip even with the point where you started stitching.

9. Tuck the end of the binding into the folded corner at the beginning. Continue sewing, ending just past the point where you started.

10. Fold the binding to the back of the quilt, being sure the fabric covers the stitched seam. Use one length of thread to blindstitch the binding down to the back of the quilt. Stitch up the through the binding fold and back down underneath the binding so your stitches are concealed.

11. Tuck in the corners as you get to them.

Index

Dedication

A quilt like this is a labor of love. I would like to dedicate this book to anyone who chooses to infuse each block with a little bit of themselves and to create a quilt using them.

In this digital age I am friends with many people that I have never met. Every day they provide me with the encouragement and validation that keeps me motivated. A very special thanks to all of you who call yourselves the Tula Troops. Thanks guys! Your creativity astounds me. When I grow up I want to be just like you.

Special thanks to Marilyn Foti, Carl Hentsch and Angela Walters for always being there when I bite off more than I can chew.

I would not be able to sit in my studio for months writing a book like this without the amazing support of a few staggeringly important people, Kathy, Cameron and Grace. You know who you are and what you do.

About the Author

Tula Pink is an American textile designer and quilt maker with a dark sense of humor buried in a sea of print and pattern. She plays with images the way a poet plays with words, turning innocuous traditional designs into mischievous little critters. Whether it's a head of hair teased into a pirate ship or a damask molded into a frog, Ms. Pink can wrangle any shape into her own candy-colored fantasy of creature delights.

Tula's love affair with textiles began early, and an obsession with sewing soon followed. It was apparent to everyone but Tula that she would eventually be designing the fabric herself. A few years and twelve fabric collections later, design is her one and only passion. Tula began quilting in an effort to use up her ever-growing stash of fabric so she could justify buying more. Sixteen years later, she has a lot of quilts and more fabric than when she started.

Tula Pink's City Sampler. Copyright © 2013 by Tula Pink. Manufactured in China. All rights reserved. No part of this book may be reproduced in any form or by any electronic or mechanical means including information storage and retrieval systems without permission in writing from the publisher, except by a reviewer who may quote brief passages in a review. Published by David & Charles, an imprint of F+W Media, Inc., 10151 Carver Road, Ste. 200, Blue Ash, Ohio 45242. (800) 289-0963. First Edition.

www.fwmedia.com

17   16   15   14   13   5   4   3   2   1

DISTRIBUTED IN CANADA BY FRASER DIRECT
100 Armstrong Avenue
Georgetown, ON, Canada L7G 5S4
Tel: (905) 877-4411

DISTRIBUTED IN THE U.K. AND EUROPE BY F&W MEDIA INTERNATIONAL
Brunel House, Newton Abbot, Devon, TQ12 4PU, England
Tel: (+44) 1626 323200, Fax: (+44) 1626 323319
E-mail: enquiries@fwmedia.com

DISTRIBUTED IN AUSTRALIA BY CAPRICORN LINK
P.O. Box 704, S. Windsor NSW, 2756 Australia
Tel: (02) 4560 1600   Fax: (02) 4577 5288
E-mail: books@capricornlink.com.au

SRN: V8200

ISBN-13: 978-1-4402-3214-5
ISBN-10: 1-4402-3214-8

Acquisitions Editor: Kelly Biscopink
Editor: Noel Rivera
Designer: Victoria Marks
Photographer: Elizabeth Maxson
Illustrator: Tula Pink

Metric Conversion Chart

To convert	to	multiply by
Inches	Centimeters	2.54
Centimeters	Inches	0.4
Feet	Centimeters	30.5
Centimeters	Feet	0.03
Yards	Meters	0.9
Meters	Yards	1.1

Make it, love it, share it!

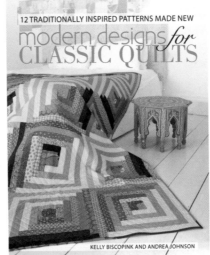

Join our online craft communities for exclusive offers and daily doses of inspiration!

Stitch Magazine
http://www.quiltingdaily.com/
blogs/stitch/home.aspx

Sew Daily
http://www.sewdaily.com/

Quilts from the House of Tula Pink
20 Fabric Projects to Make, Use & Love

by Tula Pink

Welcome to the world of cutting-edge fabric designer Tula Pink, where clever quilts show off fanciful fabric, and your imagination can be let out to play. With ten amazing quilts and ten extra-cool projects, you'll be inspired to play with fabric, color and design in a way like never before.

Modern Designs for Classic Quilts
12 Traditionally Inspired Patterns Made New

by Kelly Biscopink & Andrea Johnson

Watch as modern fabrics and inspiration combine to give traditional quilts a fresh new look. Featuring a vibrant collection of quilt patterns and projects with easy-to-follow instructions, *Modern Designs for Classic Quilts* makes creating quilts with your own personal touch simple and fun.